21ST CENTURY ROCK

PUBLISHED BY
WISE PUBLICATIONS,
8/9 FRITH STREET, LONDON,
W1D 3JB, ENGLAND.

EXCLUSIVE DISTRIBUTORS:
MUSIC SALES LIMITED
DISTRIBUTION CENTRE,
NEWMARKET ROAD, BURY ST EDMUNDS,
SUFFOLK, IP33 3YB, ENGLAND.
MUSIC SALES PTY LIMITED
120 ROTHSCHILD AVENUE, ROSEBERY,
NSW 2018, AUSTRALIA.

ORDER NO. AM89492
ISBN 0-7119-3036-8
THIS BOOK © COPYRIGHT 2004
BY WISE PUBLICATIONS.

COMPILED BY NICK CRISPIN.
MUSIC ARRANGED BY MATT COWE.
MUSIC PROCESSED BY
PAUL EWERS MUSIC DESIGN.

COVER DESIGN BY FRESH LEMON.

YOUR GUARANTEE OF QUALITY:
AS PUBLISHERS, WE STRIVE TO PRODUCE EVERY
BOOK TO THE HIGHEST COMMERCIAL STANDARDS.
THE MUSIC HAS BEEN FRESHLY ENGRAVED AND
THE BOOK HAS BEEN CAREFULLY DESIGNED
TO MINIMISE AWKWARD PAGE TURNS AND TO
MAKE PLAYING FROM IT A REAL PLEASURE.
PARTICULAR CARE HAS BEEN GIVEN TO
SPECIFYING ACID-FREE, NEUTRAL-SIZED
PAPER MADE FROM PULPS WHICH HAVE
NOT BEEN ELEMENTAL CHLORINE BLEACHED.
THIS PULP IS FROM FARMED SUSTAINABLE
FORESTS AND WAS PRODUCED WITH
SPECIAL REGARD FOR THE ENVIRONMENT.
THROUGHOUT, THE PRINTING AND BINDING HAVE
BEEN PLANNED TO ENSURE A STURDY,
ATTRACTIVE PUBLICATION WHICH
SHOULD GIVE YEARS OF ENJOYMENT.
IF YOUR COPY FAILS TO MEET OUR HIGH STANDARDS,
PLEASE INFORM US AND WE WILL GLADLY REPLACE IT.

www.MUSICSALES.COM

WISE PUBLICATIONS
LONDON / NEW YORK / PARIS / SYDNEY / COPENHAGEN / BERLIN / MADRID / TOKYO

GUITAR TABLATURE EXPLAINED

GUITAR MUSIC CAN BE NOTATED IN THREE DIFFERENT WAYS: ON A MUSICAL STAVE, IN TABLATURE AND IN RHYTHM SLASHES

RHYTHM SLASHES are written above the stave. Strum chords in the rhythm indicated. Round noteheads indicate single notes.

THE MUSICAL STAVE shows pitches and rhythms and is divided by lines into bars. Pitches are named after the first seven letters of the alphabet.

TABLATURE graphically represents the guitar fingerboard. Each horizontal line represents a string, and each number represents a fret.

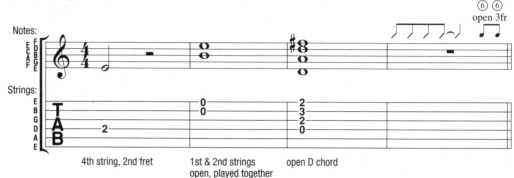

4th string, 2nd fret · 1st & 2nd strings open, played together · open D chord

DEFINITIONS FOR SPECIAL GUITAR NOTATION

SEMI-TONE BEND: Strike the note and bend up a semi-tone (1/2 step).

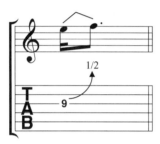

WHOLE-TONE BEND: Strike the note and bend up a whole-tone (whole step).

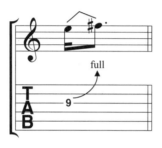

GRACE NOTE BEND: Strike the note and bend as indicated. Play the first note as quickly as possible.

QUARTER-TONE BEND: Strike the note and bend up a 1/4 step.

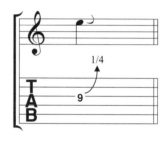

BEND & RELEASE: Strike the note and bend up as indicated, then release back to the original note.

COMPOUND BEND & RELEASE: Strike the note and bend up and down in the rhythm indicated.

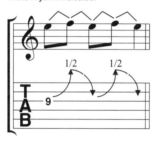

PRE-BEND: Bend the note as indicated, then strike it.

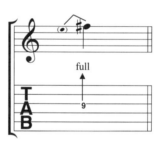

PRE-BEND & RELEASE: Bend the note as indicated. Strike it and release the note back to the original pitch.

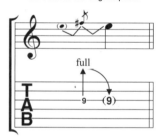

HAMMER-ON: Strike the first note with one finger, then sound the second note (on the same string) with another finger by fretting it without picking.

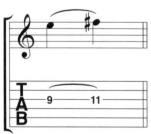

PULL-OFF: Place both fingers on the notes to be sounded, strike the first note and without picking, pull the finger off to sound the second note.

LEGATO SLIDE (GLISS): Strike the first note and then slide the same fret-hand finger up or down to the second note. The second note is not struck.

MUFFLED STRINGS: A percussive sound is produced by laying the fret hand across the string(s) without depressing, and striking them with the pick hand.

NATURAL HARMONIC: Strike the note while the fret-hand lightly touches the string directly over the fret indicated.

PICK SCRAPE: The edge of the pick is rubbed down (or up) the string, producing a scratchy sound.

PALM MUTING: The note is partially muted by the pick hand lightly touching the string(s) just before the bridge.

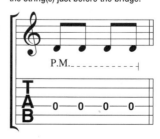

SHIFT SLIDE (GLISS & RESTRIKE): Same as legato slide, except the second note is struck.

NOTE: The speed of any bend is indicated by the music notation and tempo.

2

ASSESSMENT

WORDS & MUSIC BY RICHARD GREENTREE, ROBIN JONES, JOHN MACLEAN & STEPHEN MASON

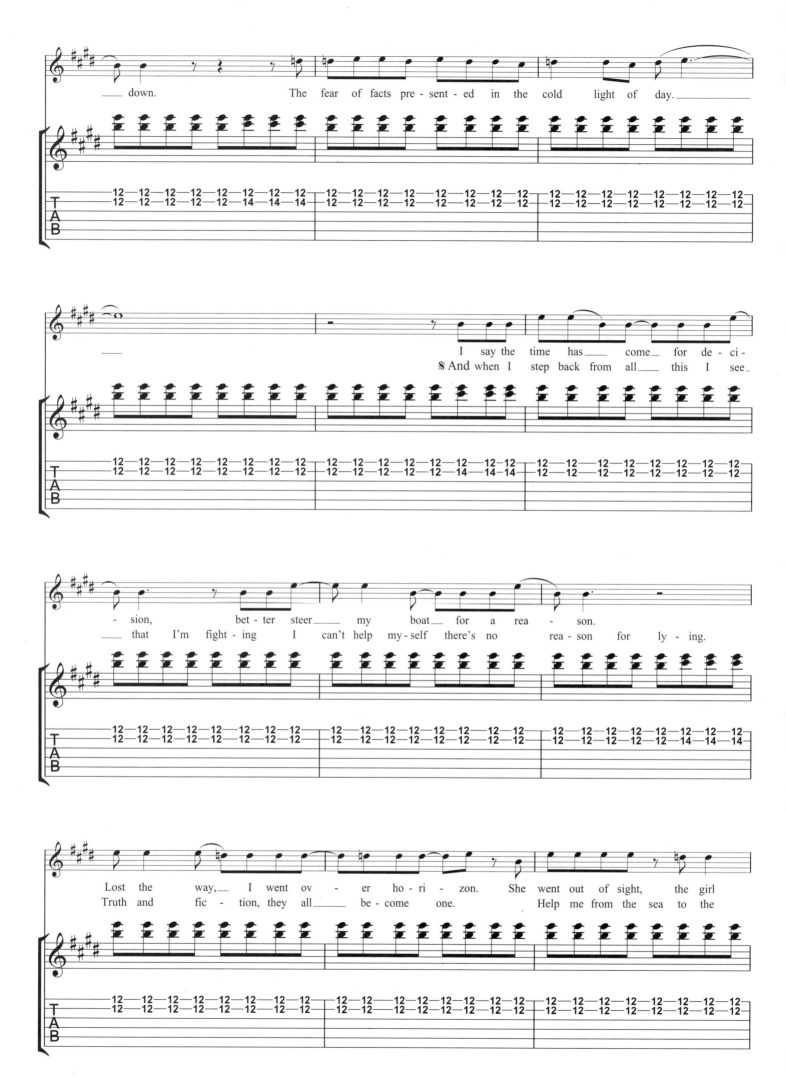

down. The fear of facts pre- sent- ed in the cold light of day.

I say the time has come for de- ci-
℅ And when I step back from all this I see

- sion, bet- ter steer my boat for a rea- son.
that I'm fight- ing I can't help my- self there's no rea- son for ly- ing.

Lost the way, I went ov- er ho- ri- zon. She went out of sight, the girl
Truth and fic- tion, they all be- come one. Help me from the sea to the

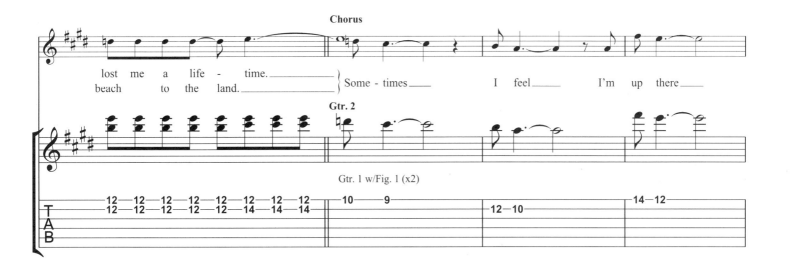

Chorus

lost me a life - time. _____ Some - times ____ I feel ____ I'm up there ____
beach to the land. _____

Gtr. 2

Gtr. 1 w/Fig. 1 (x2)

To Coda ⊕

ba - by. ____ Some- times ____ I feel ____ I'm up there ____ ba - by. ____ I say the

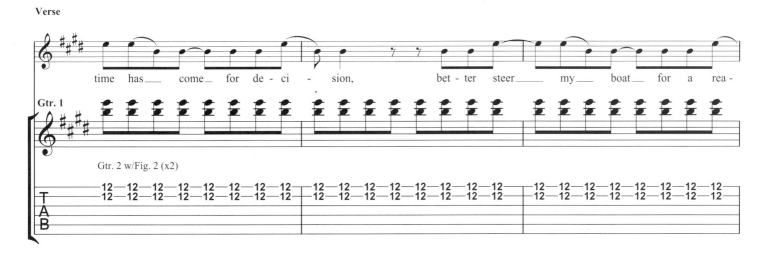

Verse

time has ____ come ____ for de - ci - sion, bet - ter steer ____ my ____ boat for a rea -

Gtr. 1

Gtr. 2 w/Fig. 2 (x2)

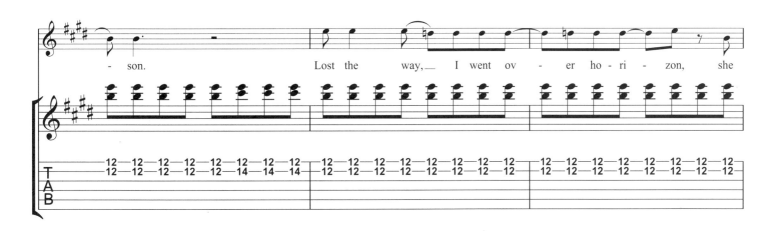

- son. Lost the way, I went ov - er ho - ri - zon, she

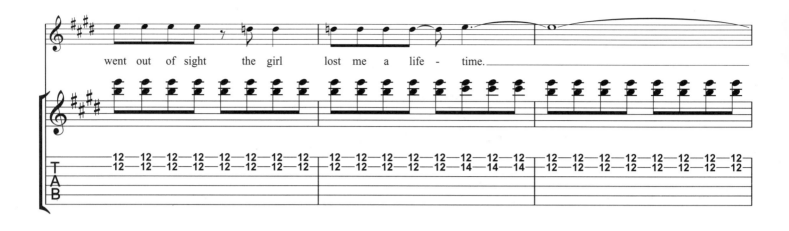

went out of sight   the girl   lost me a life - time._____

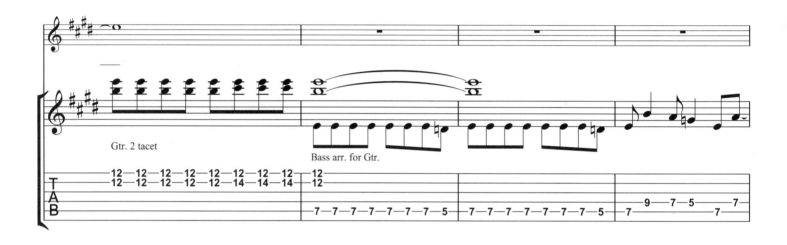

Gtr. 2 tacet

Bass arr. for Gtr.

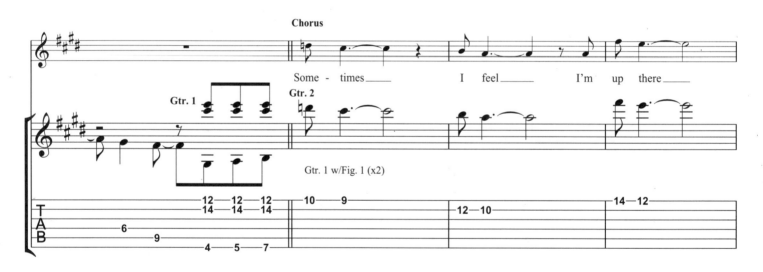

Chorus

Some - times_____   I feel_____   I'm   up   there_____

Gtr. 1   Gtr. 2

Gtr. 1 w/Fig. 1 (x2)

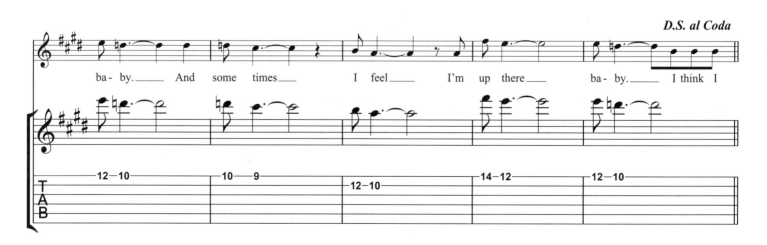

D.S. al Coda

ba - by._____ And some times_____   I feel_____   I'm   up there_____   ba - by._____ I think   I

6

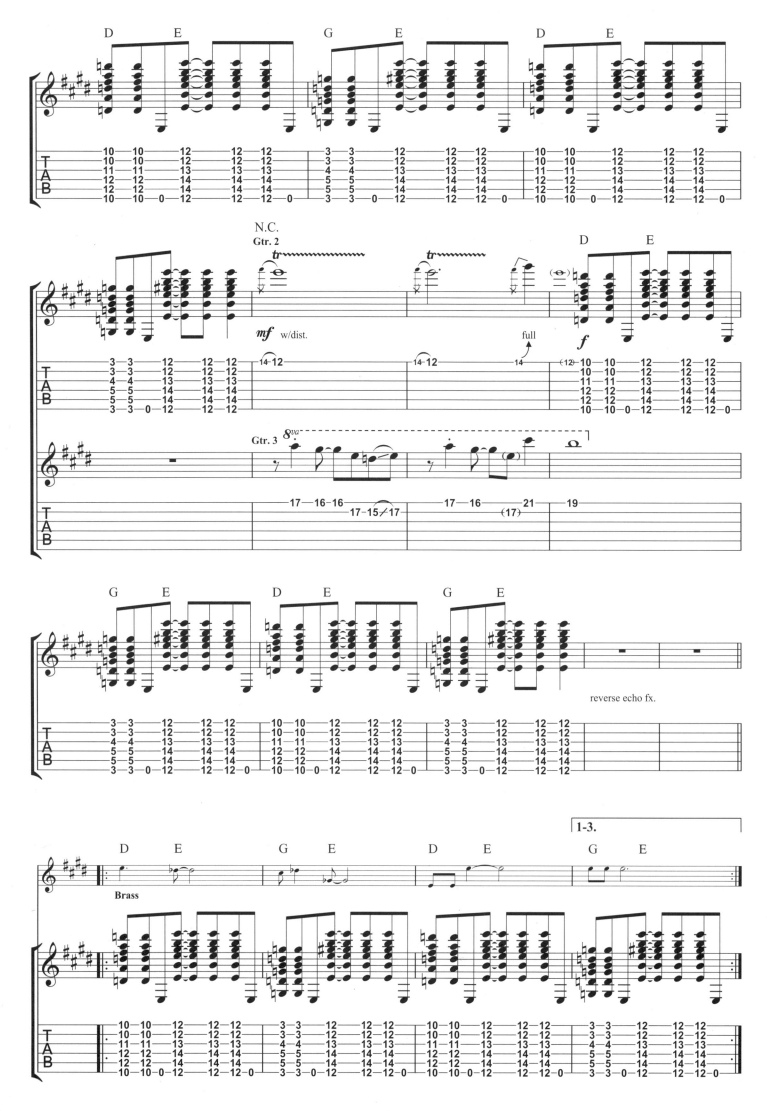

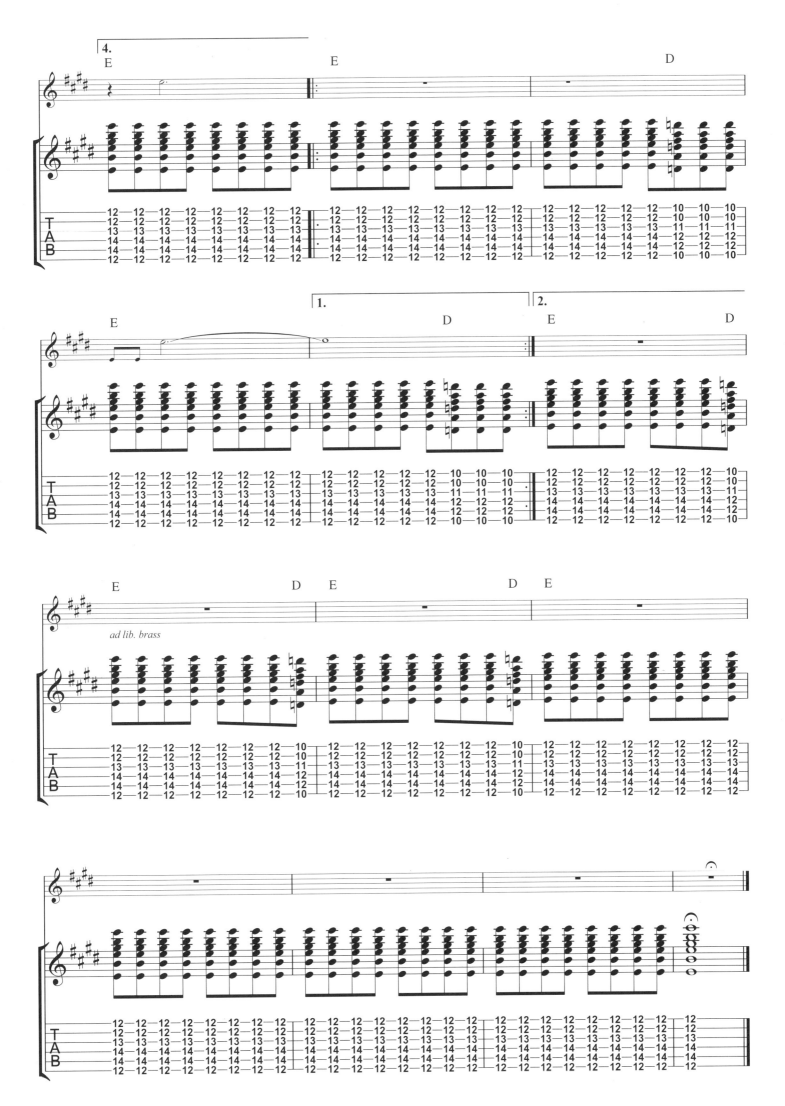

BIG SUR

WORDS BY CONOR DEASY
MUSIC BY CONOR DEASY, KEVIN HORAN, PADRAIC McMAHON, DANIEL RYAN & BEN CARRIGAN
CONTAINS ELEMENTS FROM "THEME FROM THE MONKEES" –
WORDS & MUSIC BY TOMMY BOYCE & BOBBY HART

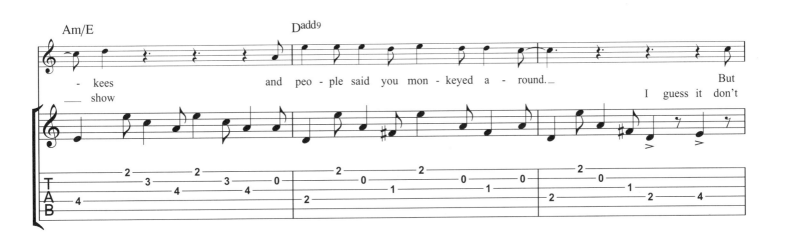

Chorus

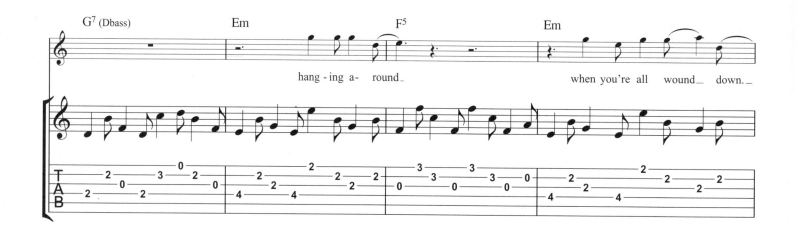

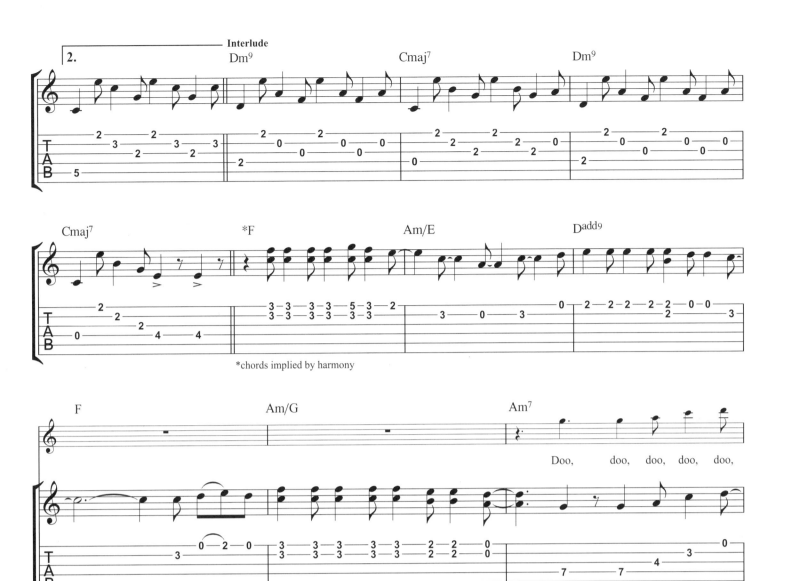

*chords implied by harmony

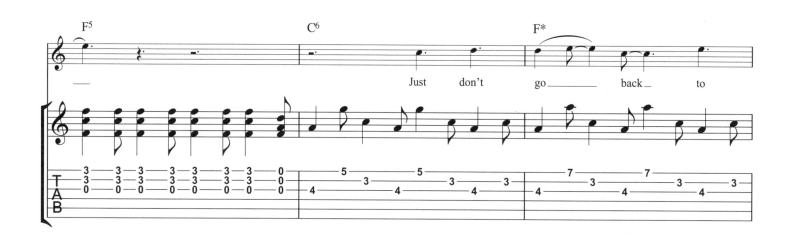

THE BITTER END

WORDS & MUSIC BY BRIAN MOLKO, STEFAN OLSDAL & STEVE HEWITT

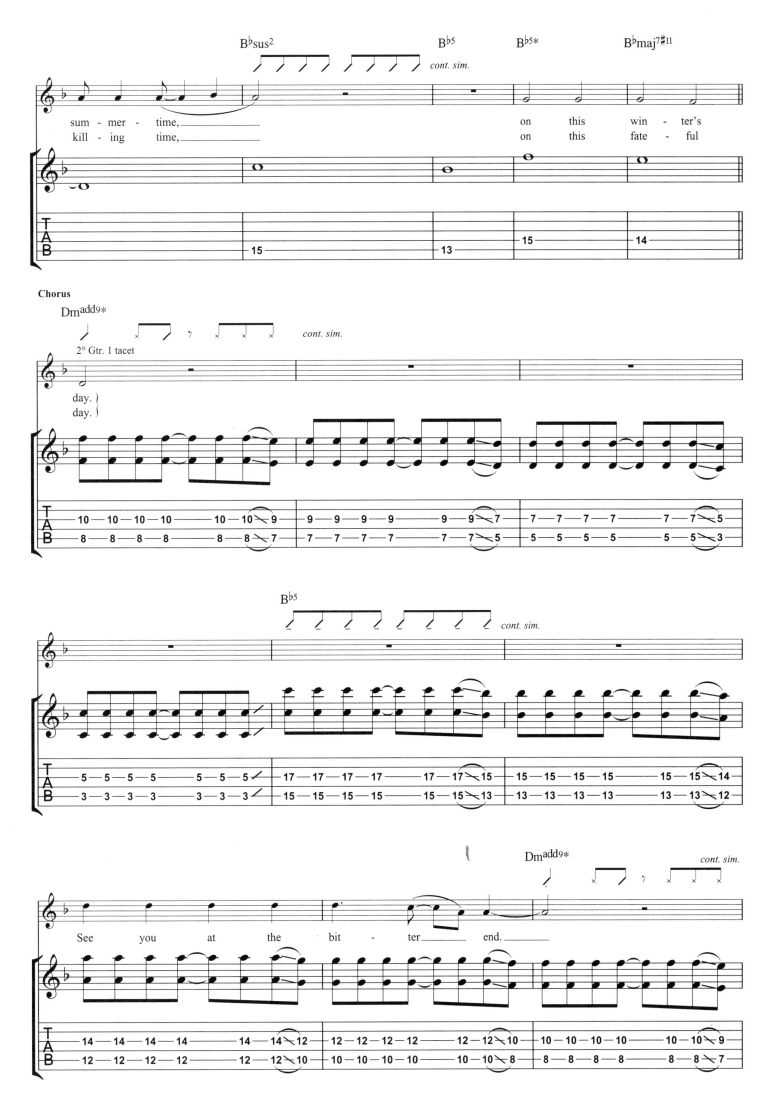

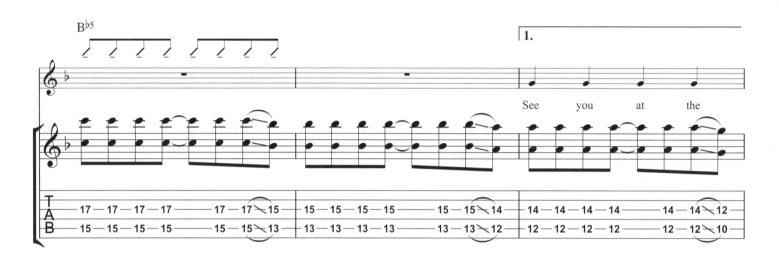

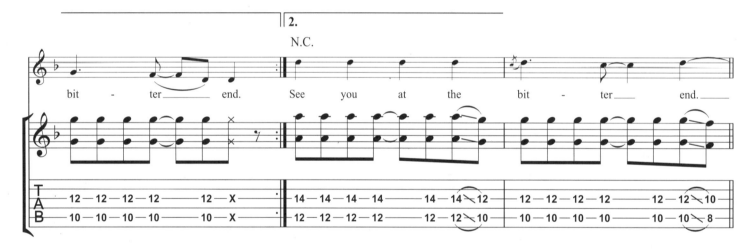

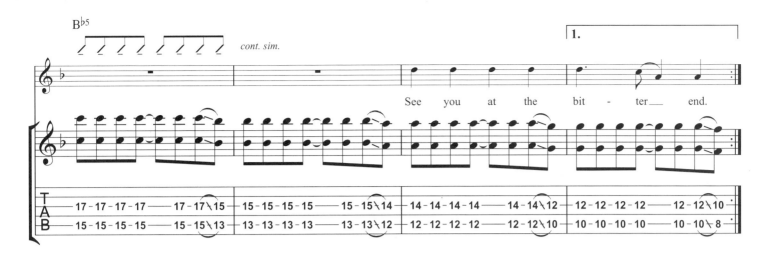

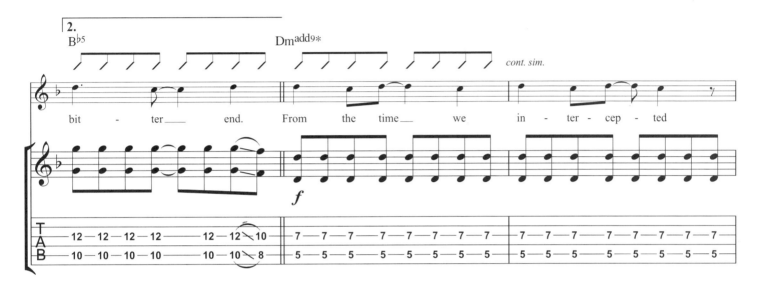

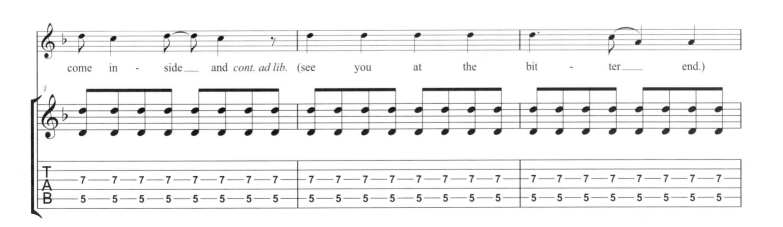

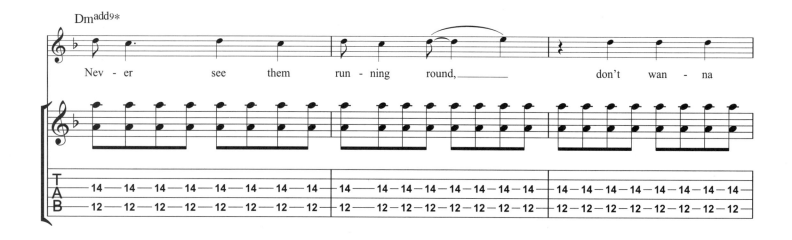

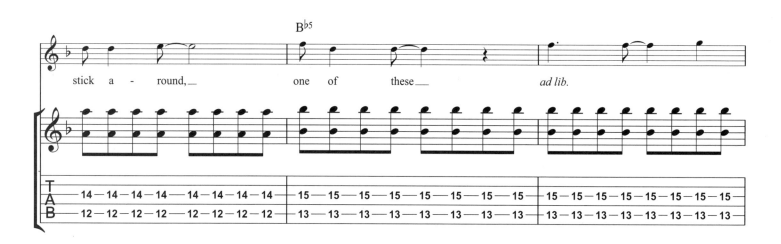

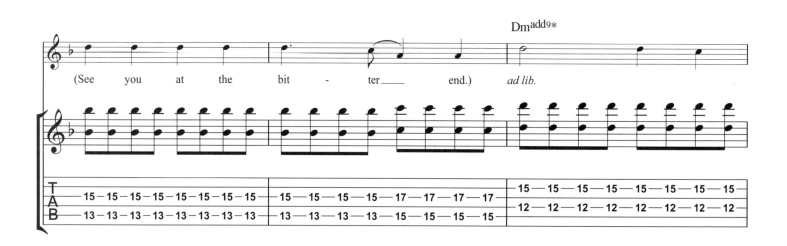

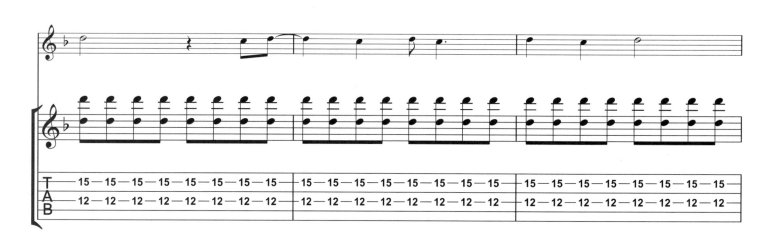

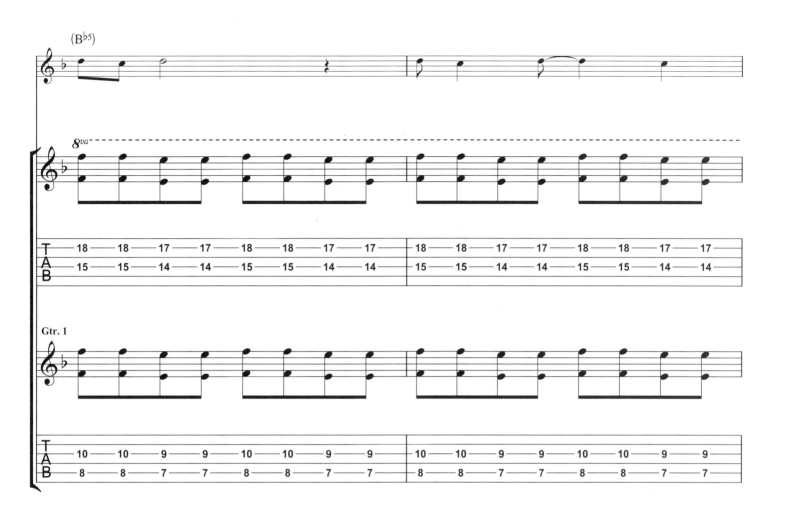

(See you at the bit - ter___ end.)___

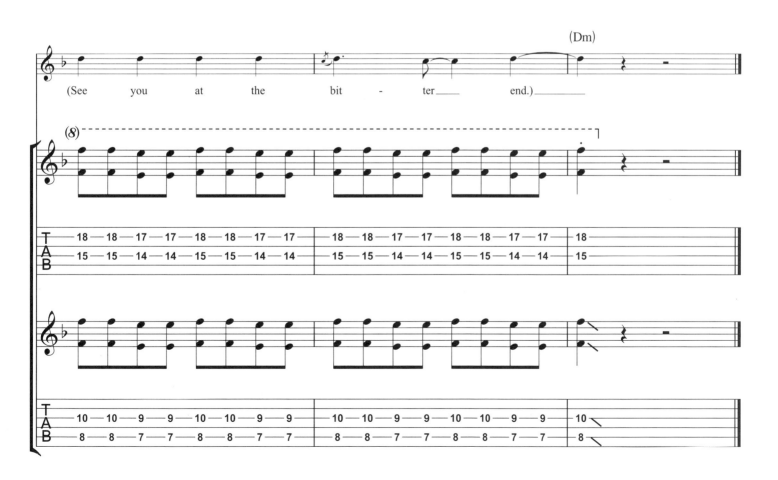

BORN AGAIN

WORDS & MUSIC BY DAMON GOUGH

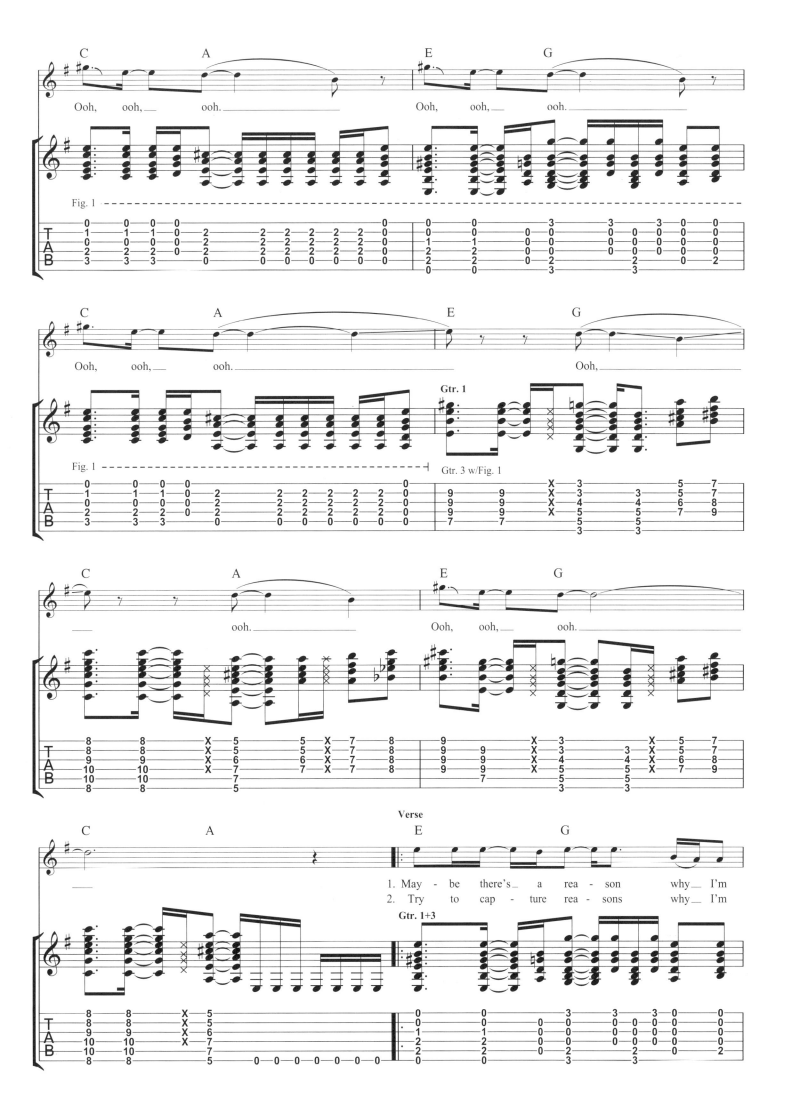

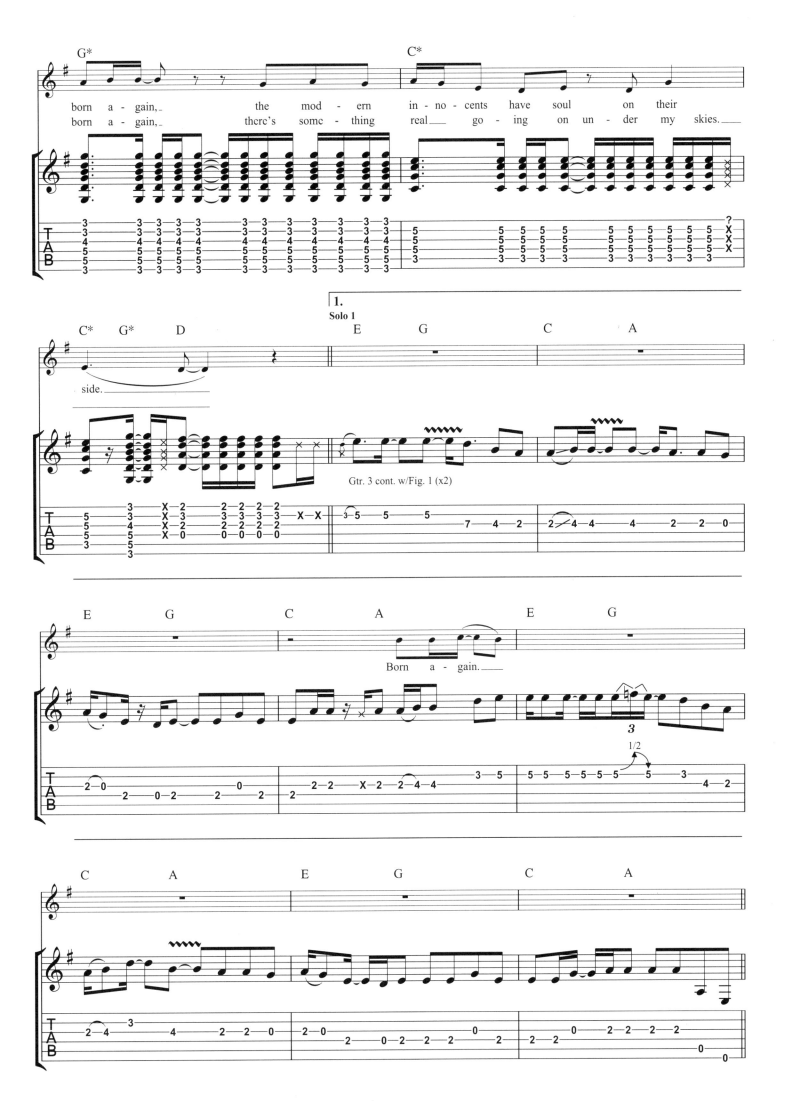

born a - gain,___ the mod - ern in - no - cents have soul on their

born a - gain,___ there's some - thing real___ go - ing on un - der my skies.___

1.

Solo 1

side.___

Gtr. 3 cont. w/Fig. 1 (x2)

Born a - gain.___

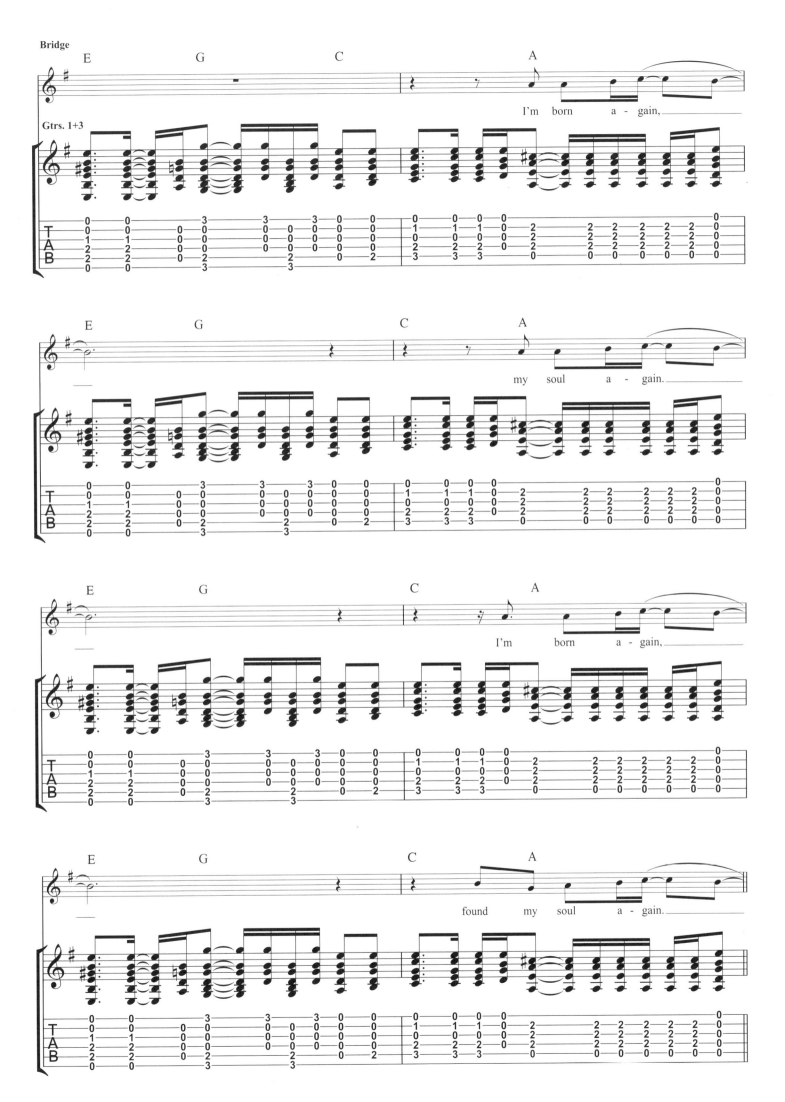

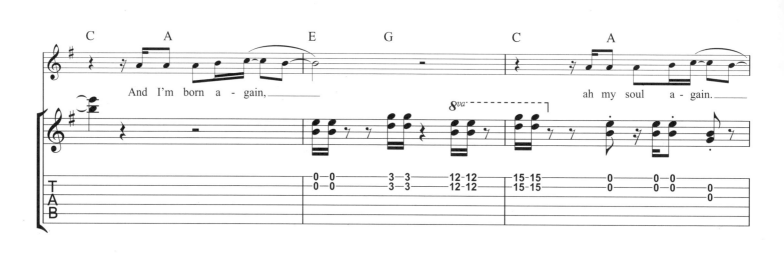

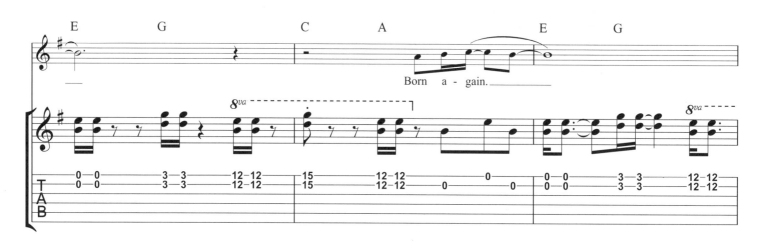

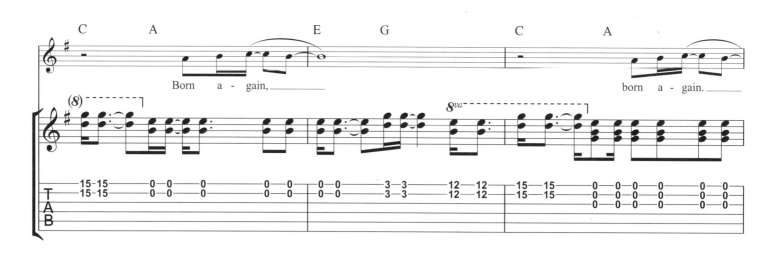

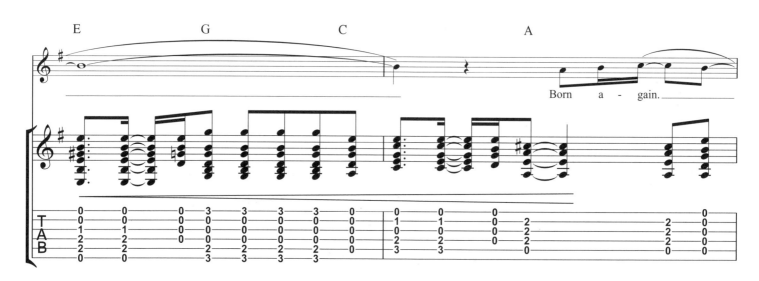

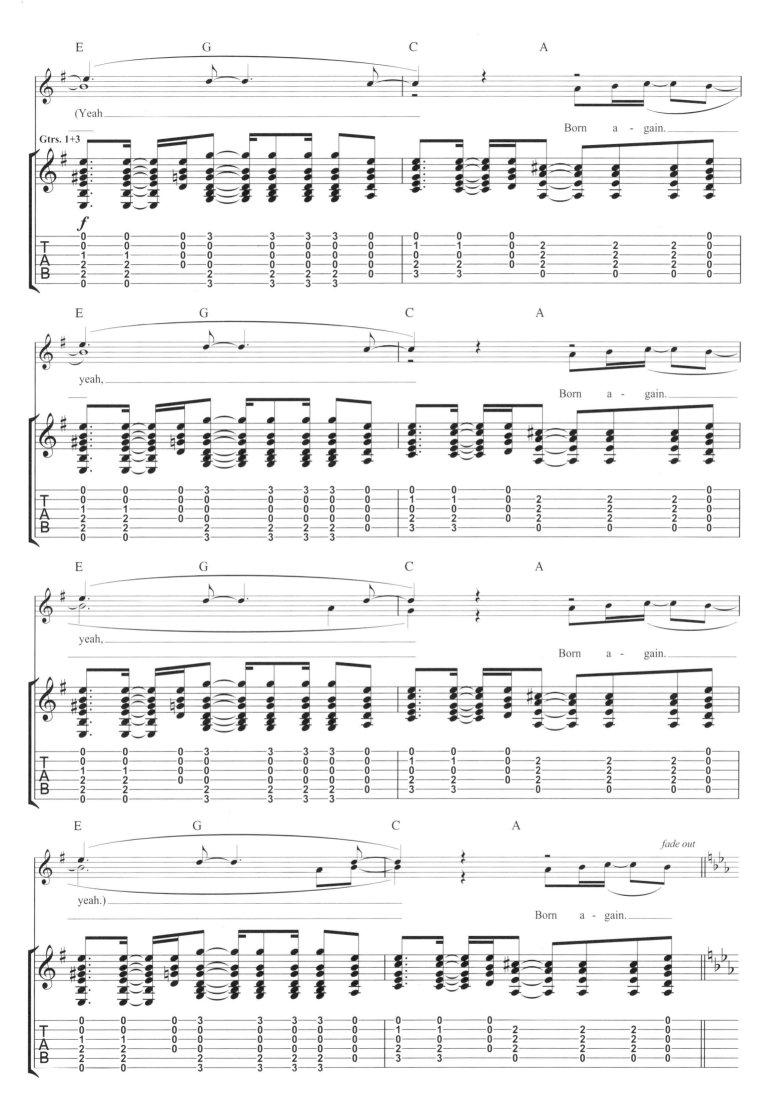

California Waiting

Words & Music by Caleb Followill, Nathan Followill & Angelo Petraglia

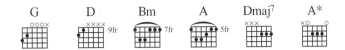

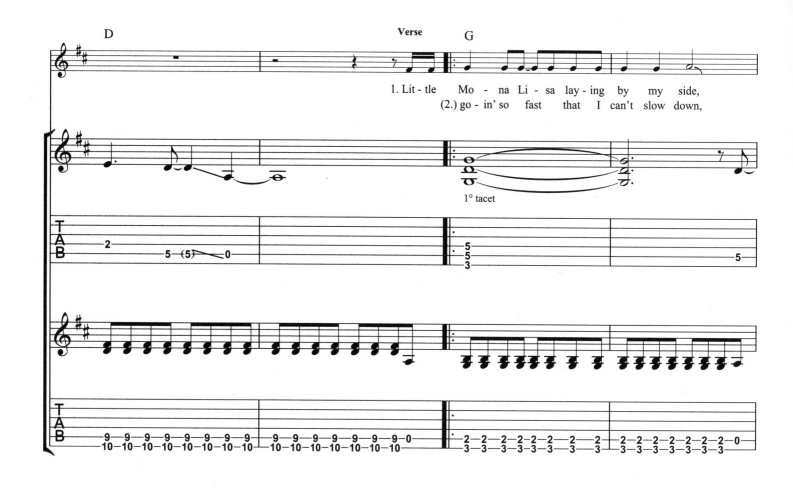

1. Lit - tle   Mo - na Li - sa lay - ing by   my   side,
(2.) go - in' so   fast   that   I   can't   slow   down,

1° tacet

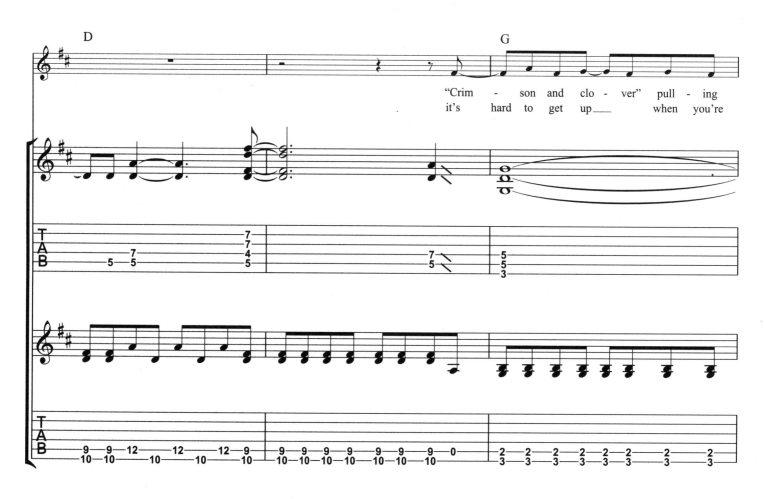

"Crim - son and clo - ver" pull - ing
it's   hard   to   get   up___   when   you're

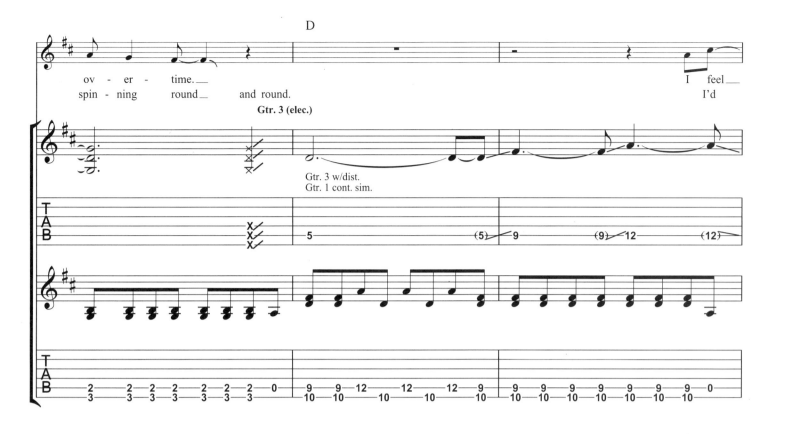

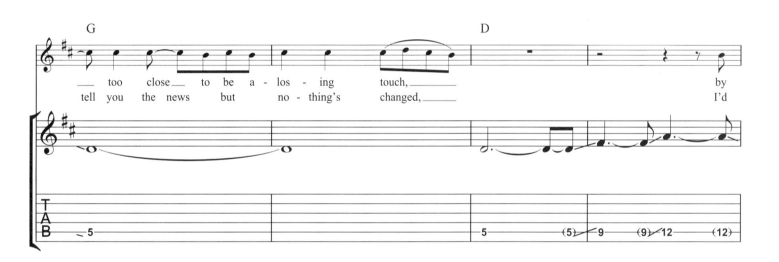

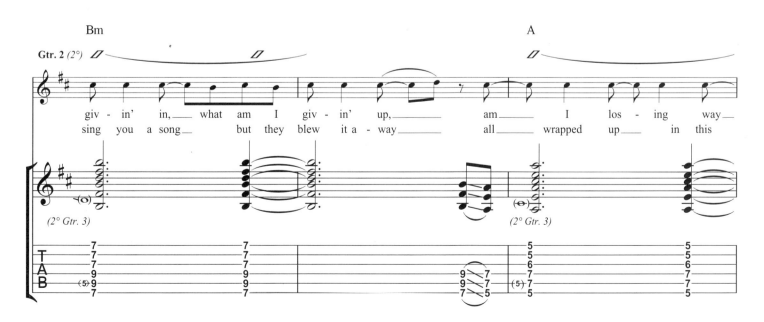

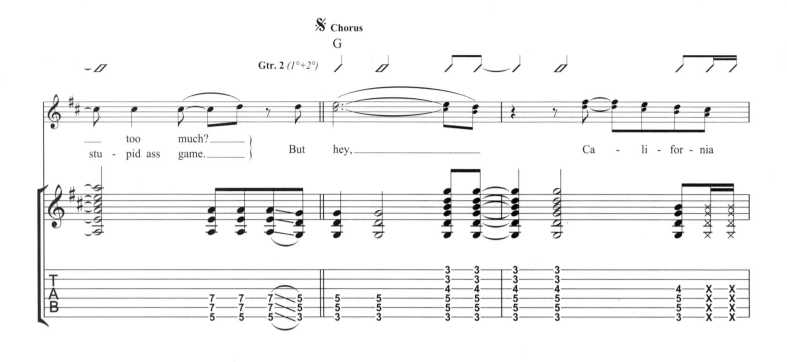

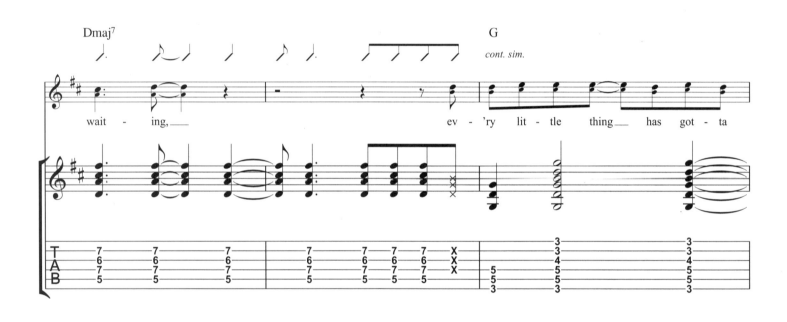

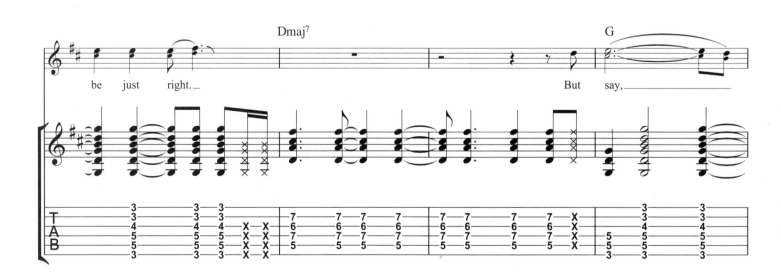

Dmaj7 — while___ you're try'n' to save me,___ why

G — can't I go 'bout___ oh my lone-ly life?___ Dmaj7

1. 2. Bridge — A* — cont. ad lib. sim.

2. I'm — Gtr. 3 — Gtrs. 1+2 cont. in slashes

COLOURS IN WAVES

WORDS & MUSIC BY JOEL CADBURY, JAMES McDONALD & BRETT SHAW

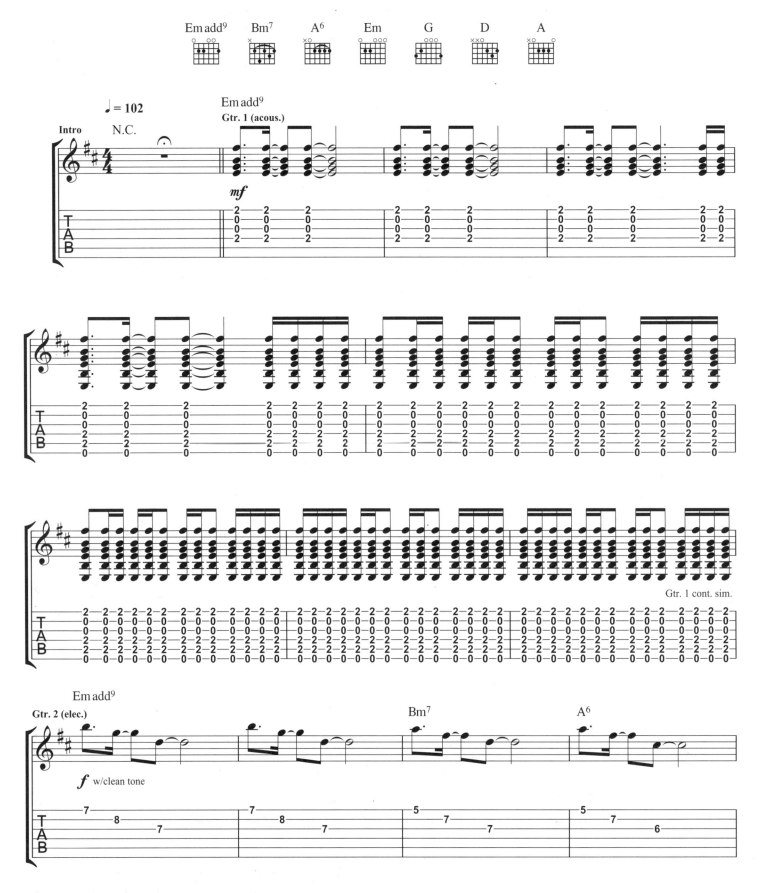

cuts my __ heart, __ know - ing __ that __ the time __ is passed. __

Comes in __ waves __ that don't be - long, __ to me they're __

Chorus

si - lent. Fall back __ on what you've __ done, __

I'll be __ the on - ly __ one. These col - ours __ be -

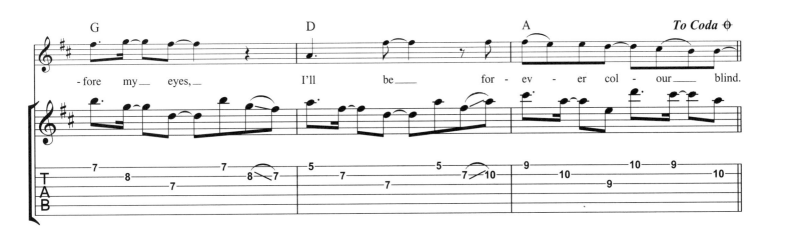

-fore my_ eyes,_ I'll be_ for - ev - er col - our_ blind.

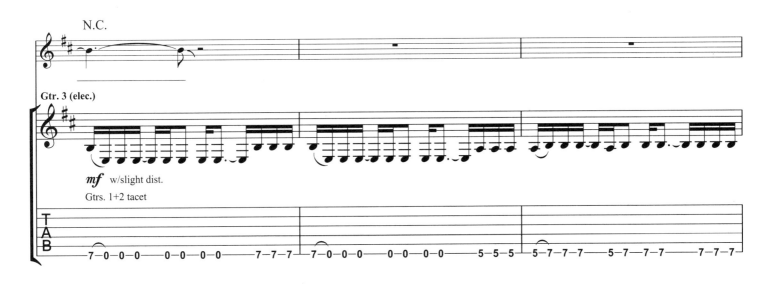

Gtr. 3 (elec.)

mf w/slight dist.

Gtrs. 1+2 tacet

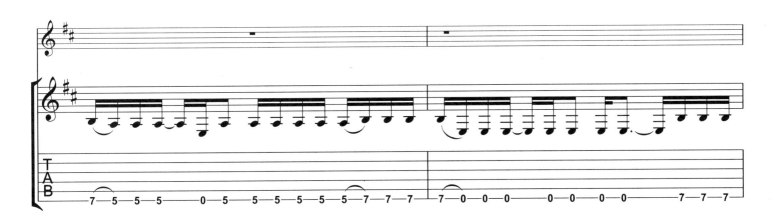

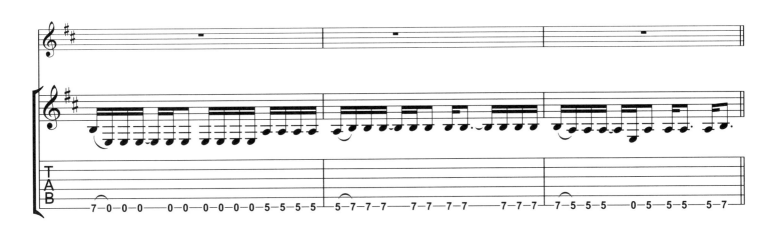

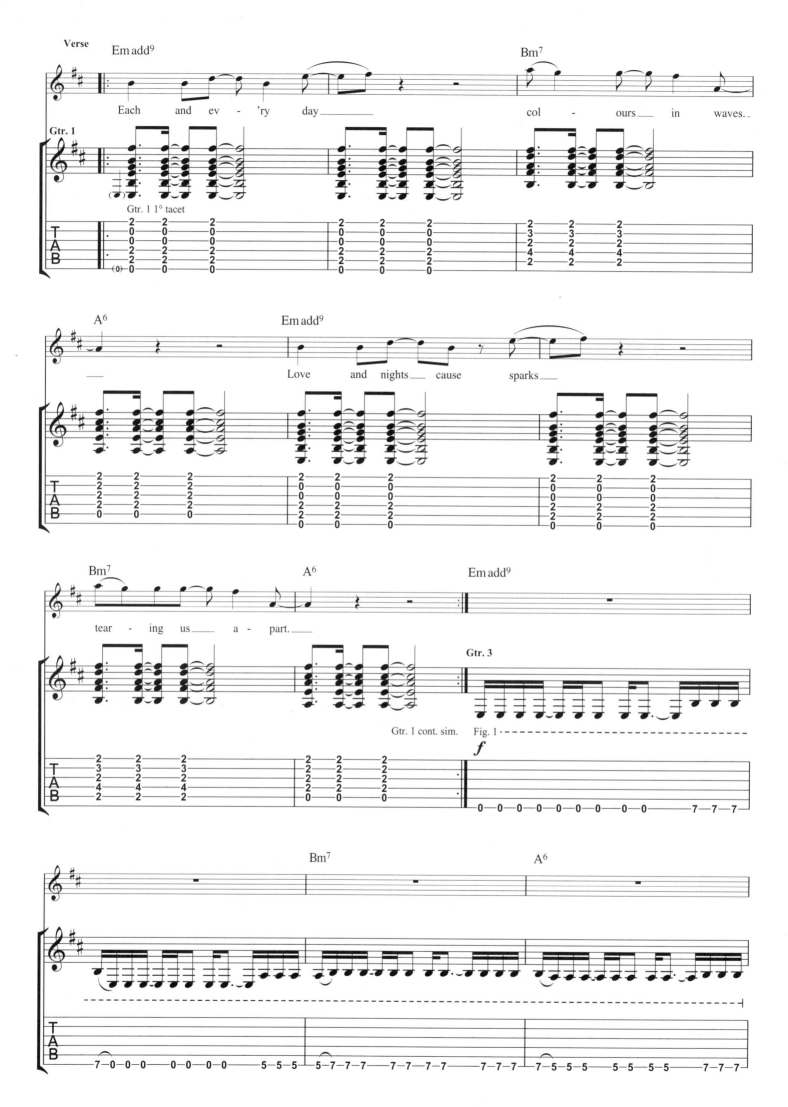

COMFORT IN SOUND

WORDS & MUSIC BY GRANT NICHOLAS

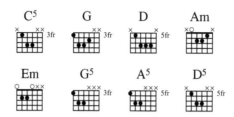

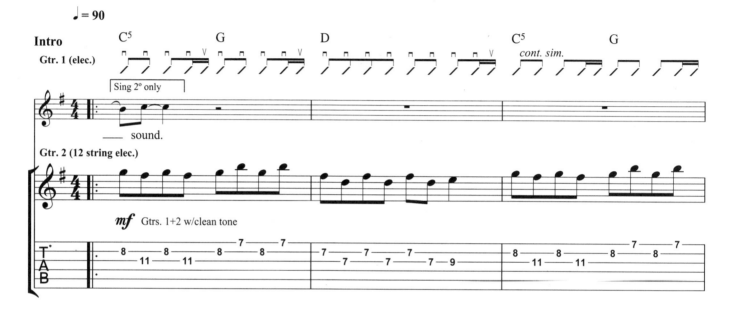

1. We fall right in_____ and suf - fer the sins,_____
2. We suf - fer love_____ to - ge - ther as one,_____
3. So - lu - tion gone,_____ e - mo - tions a - blaze,

Chorus

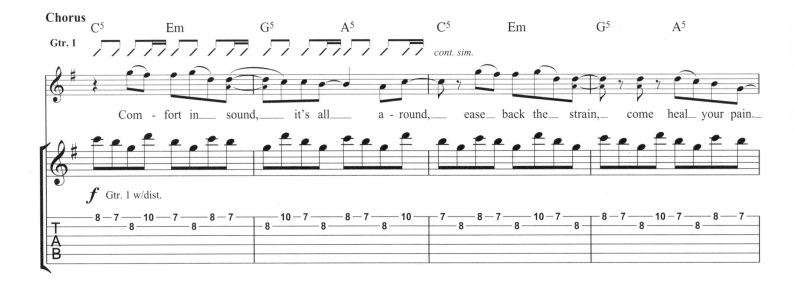

Com - fort in sound, it's all a - round, ease back the strain, come heal your pain.

f Gtr. 1 w/dist.

Com - fort in sound, it's all a - round you now. Com - fort in

Middle 8

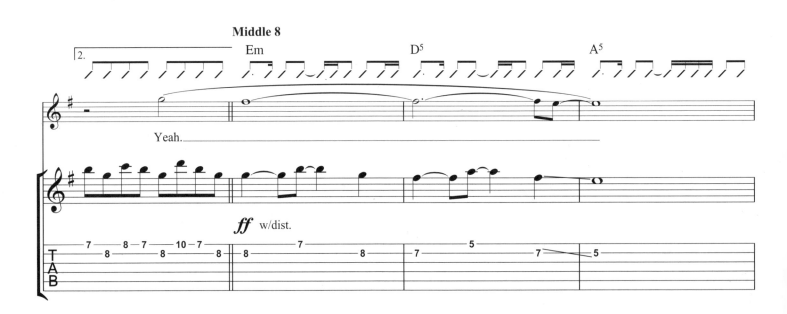

Yeah.

ff w/dist.

DANGER! HIGH VOLTAGE

WORDS & MUSIC BY TYLER SPENCER, JOSEPH FREZZA, STEPHEN NAWARA & ANTHONY SELPH

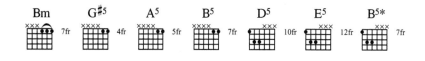

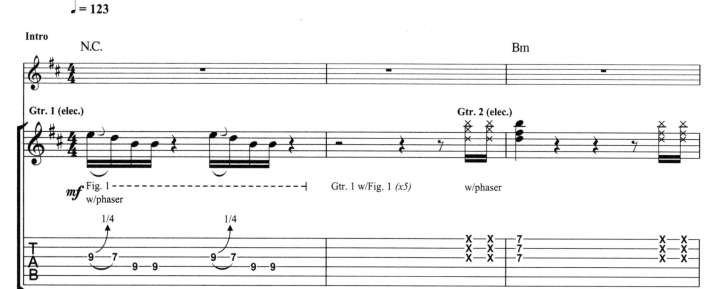

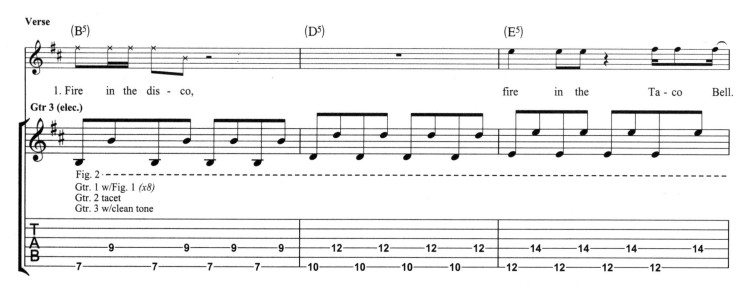

Fire in the dis - co,

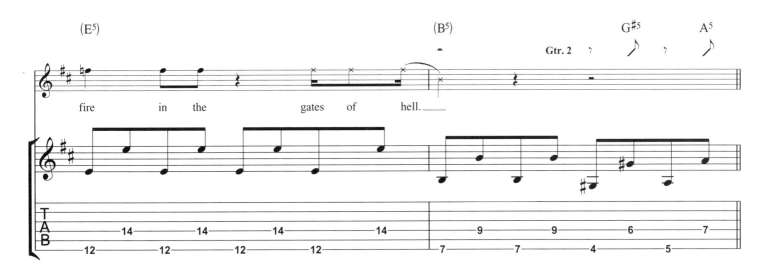

fire in the gates of hell. ___

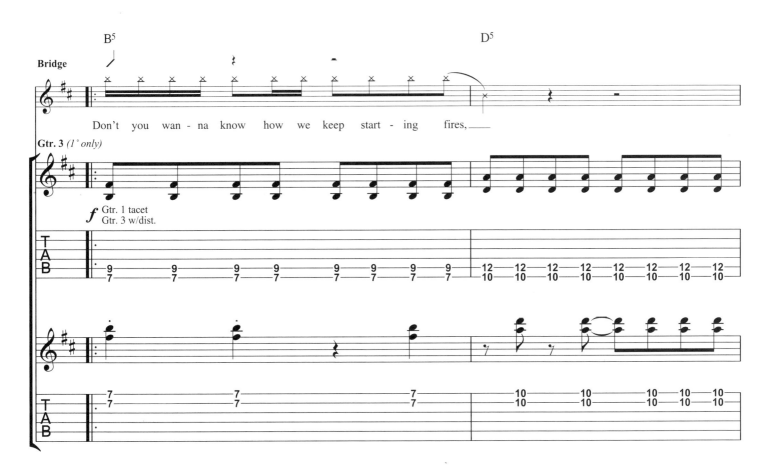

Bridge

Don't you wan - na know how we keep start - ing fires, ___

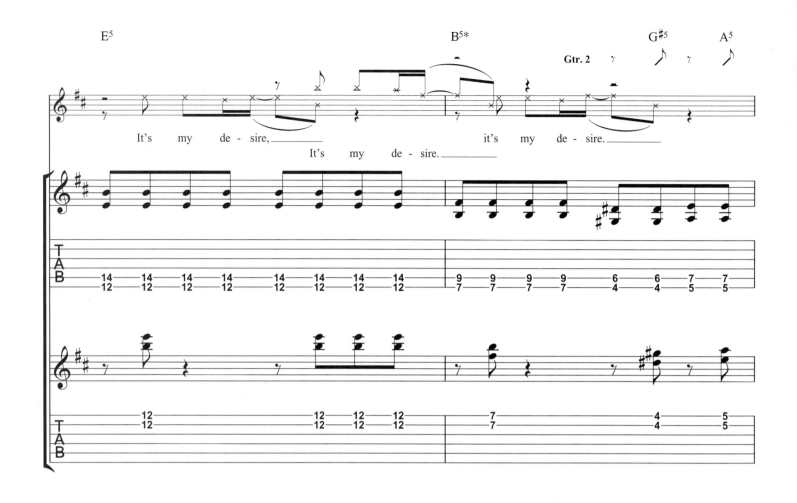

It's my de-sire,_____ it's my de-sire._____
It's my de-sire._____

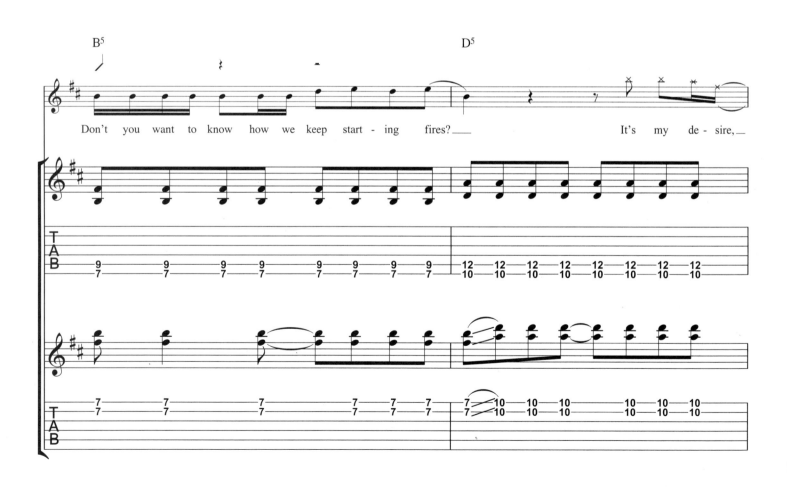

Don't you want to know how we keep start - ing fires?____ It's my de-sire,__

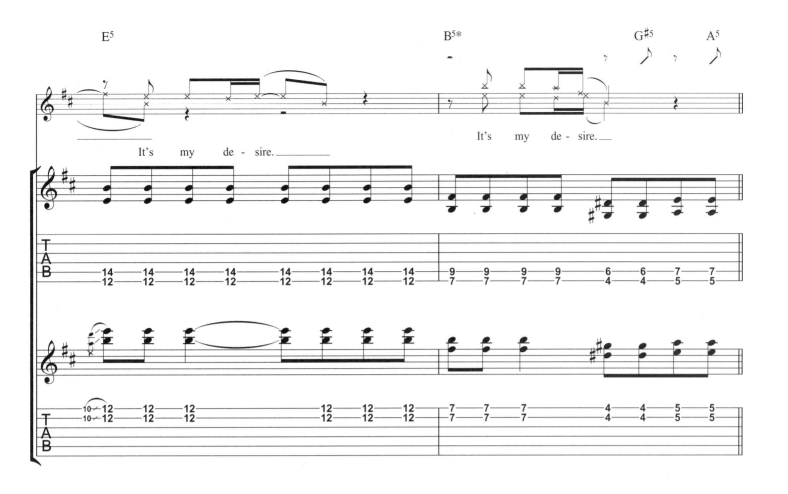

It's my de - sire.

It's my de - sire.

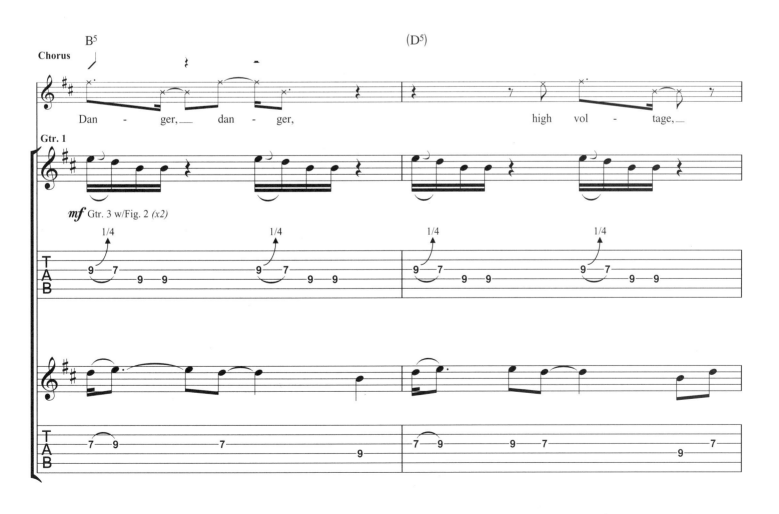

Chorus

Dan - ger, dan - ger, high vol - tage,

Gtr. 1

mf Gtr. 3 w/Fig. 2 *(x2)*

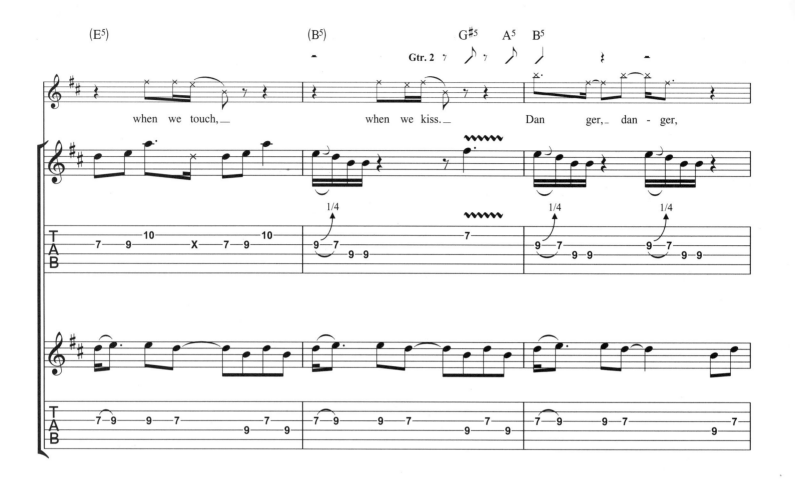

when we touch, _____ when we kiss. ____ Dan - ger, dan - ger,

high vol - tage, ___ when we touch, ___ when we kiss, ___ when we touch. ___

FEELING THE LOVE

WORDS & MUSIC BY DAVID O'BRIEN, EWAN O'BRIEN, KEVIN BROWNE & EVAN JENKINS

Chorus

Could I be dream - ing, you're touch - ing, I'm feel - ing the love

as it flows through the air.

Light - ing my fire, ig - i - ting de - sire, it's hot -

- ter than hea - ven in here.

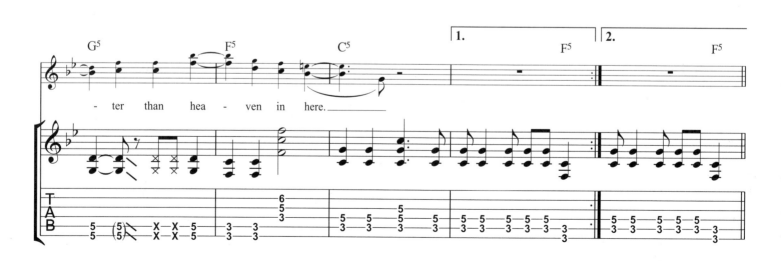

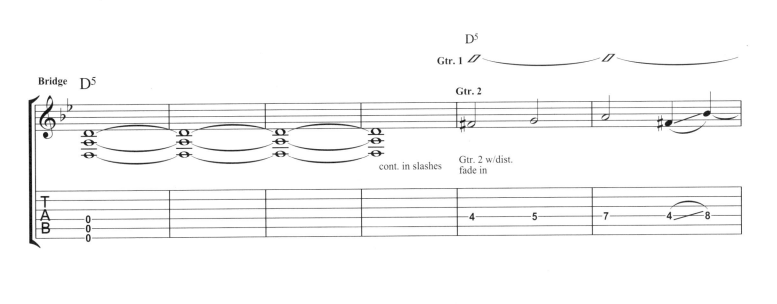

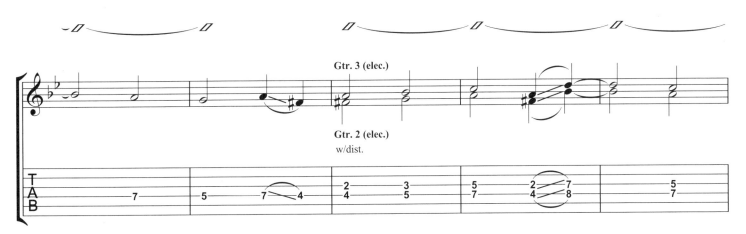

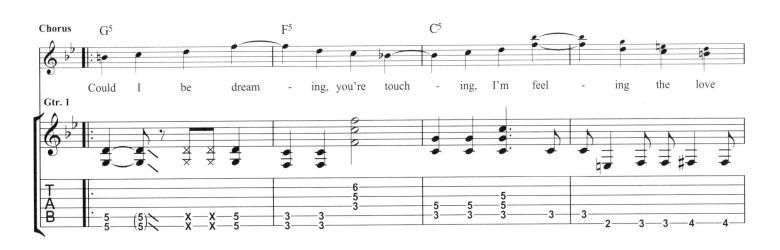

Could I be dream - ing, you're touch - ing, I'm feel - ing the love

as it flows____ through the air.____

Light - ing my fire,_____ ig - i - - ting de - sire,____

_____ it's hot - ter than hea - ven in here.____

(Indian harmonium ad lib.)

GET OFF

WORDS & MUSIC BY COURTNEY TAYLOR-TAYLOR

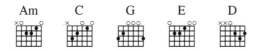

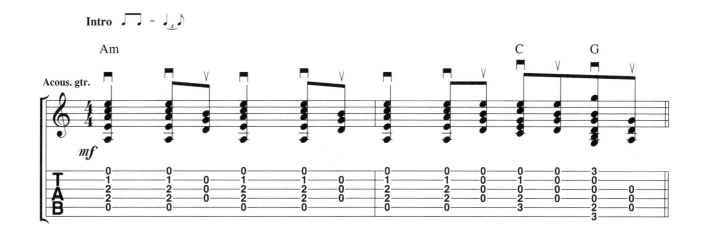

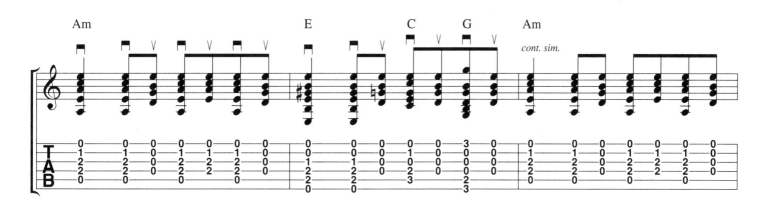

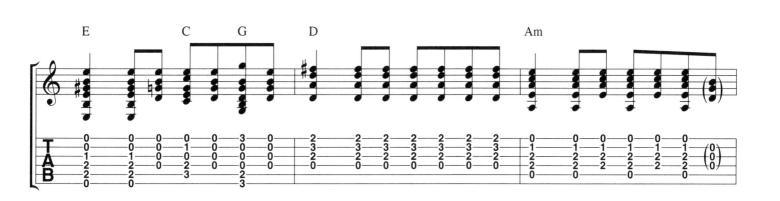

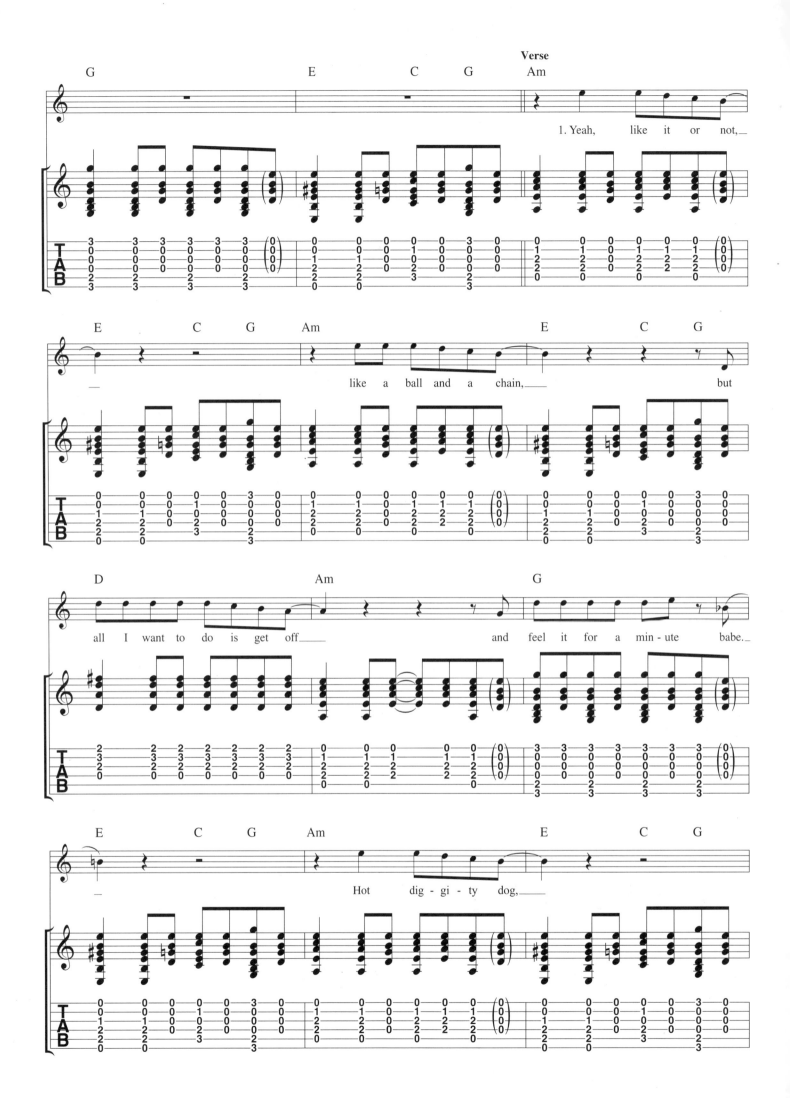

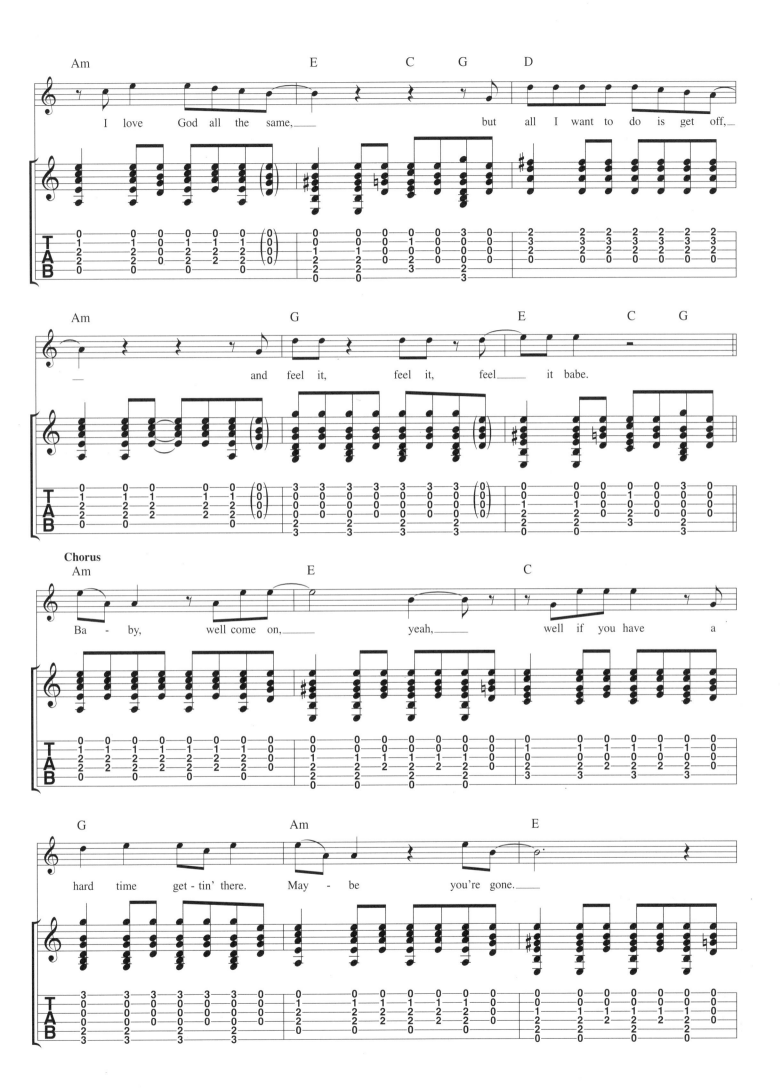

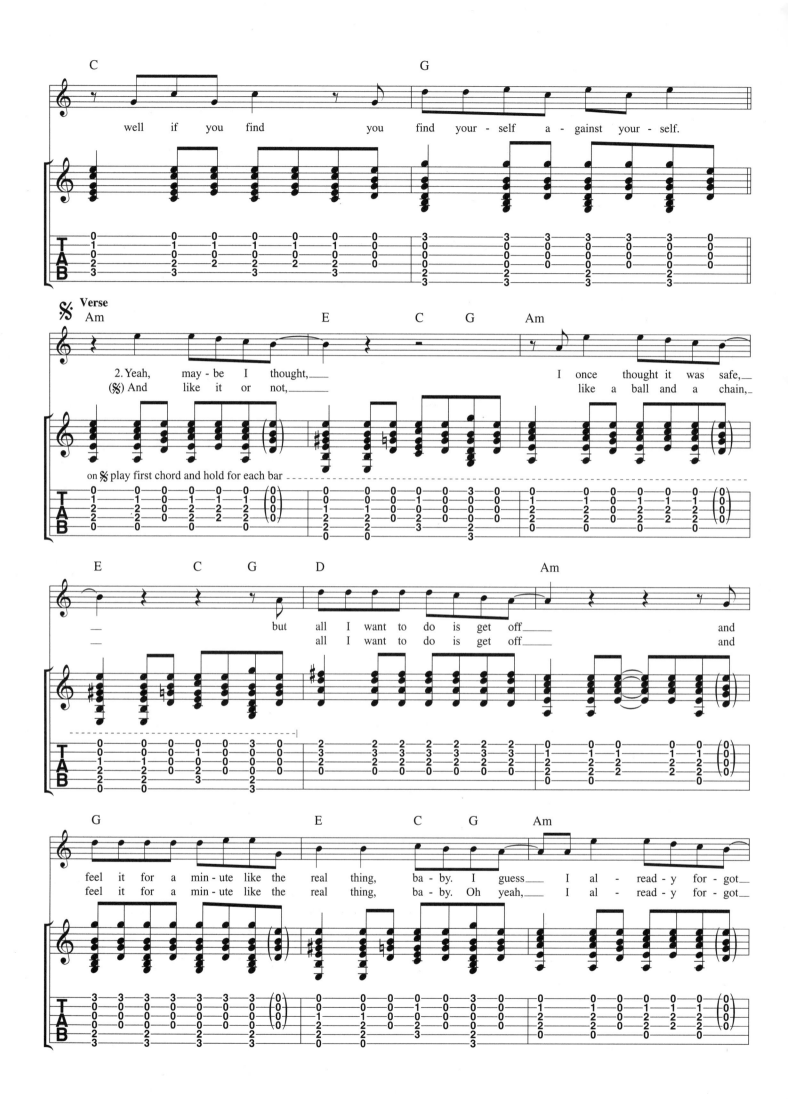

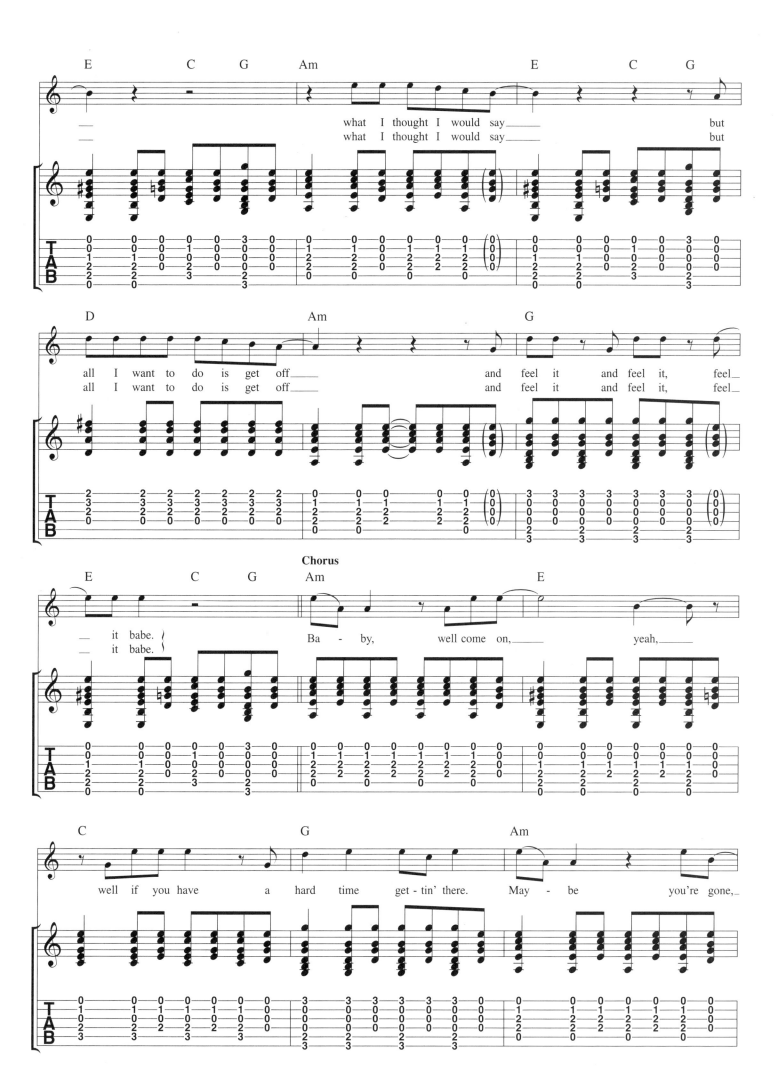

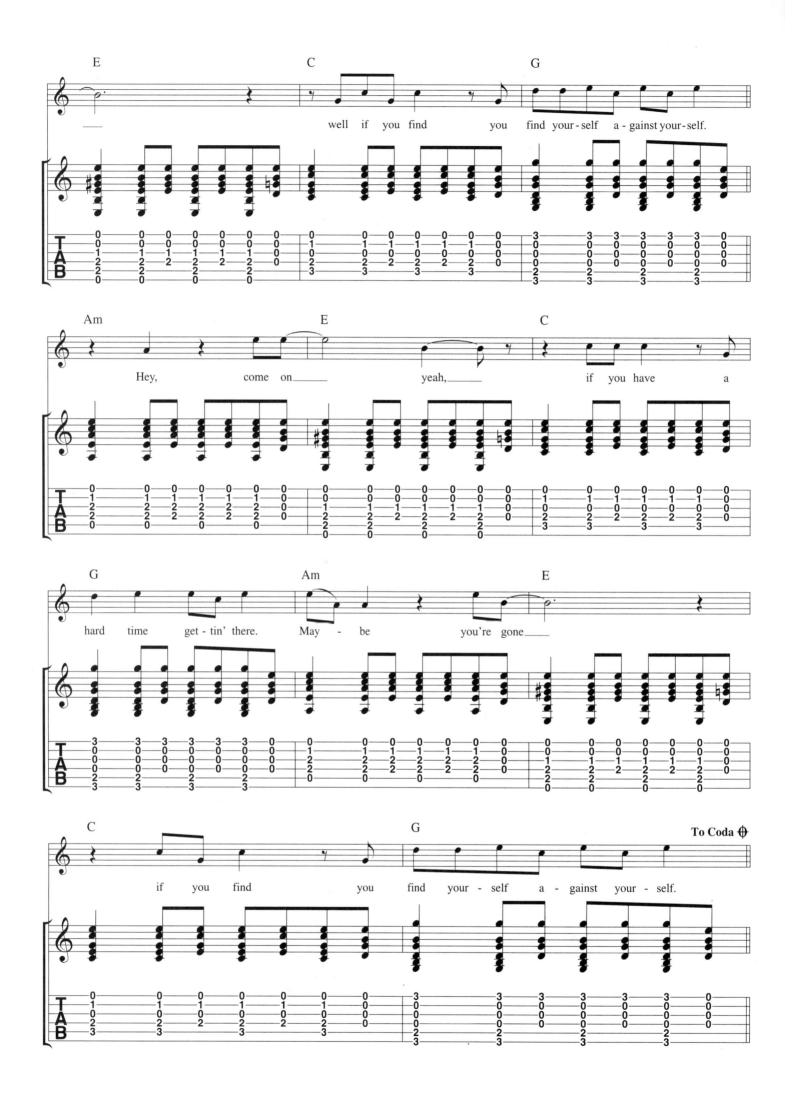

well if you find   you find your - self a - gainst your - self.

Hey,   come on____   yeah,____   if you have   a

hard time get - tin' there.   May - be   you're gone____

if you find   you find your - self a - gainst your - self.

To Coda ⊕

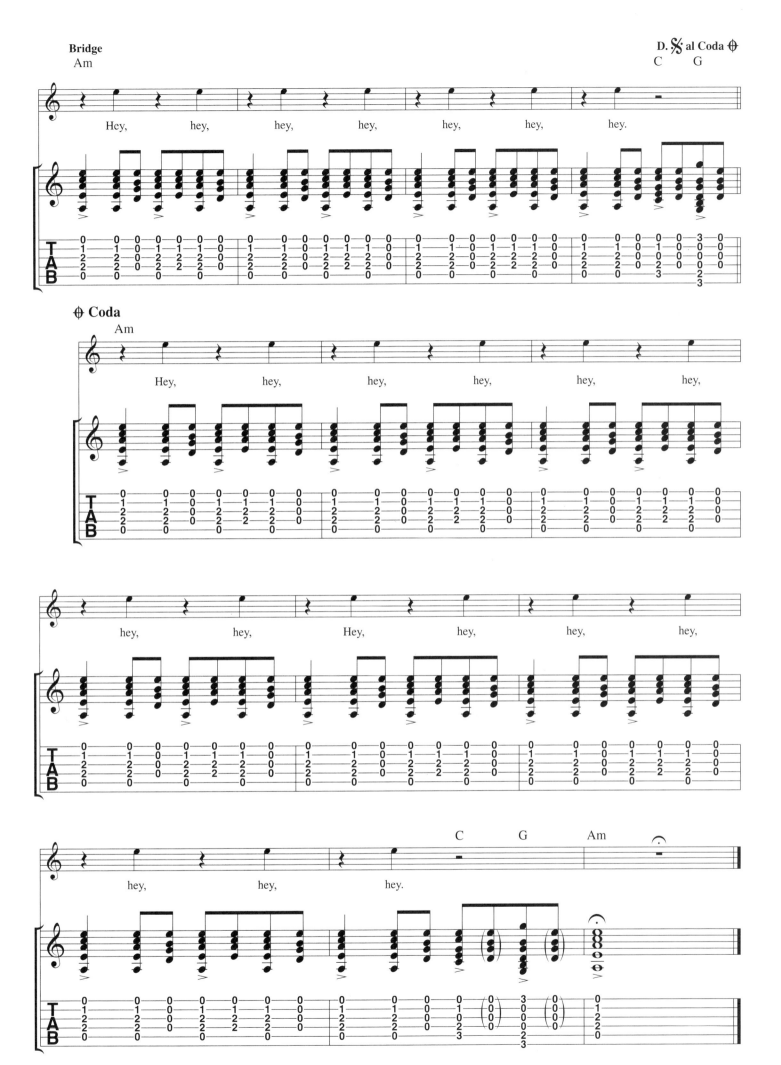

GO WITH THE FLOW

WORDS & MUSIC BY JOSH HOMME & NICK OLIVERI

Verse

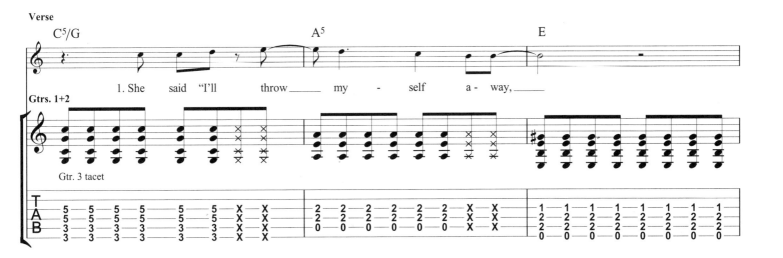

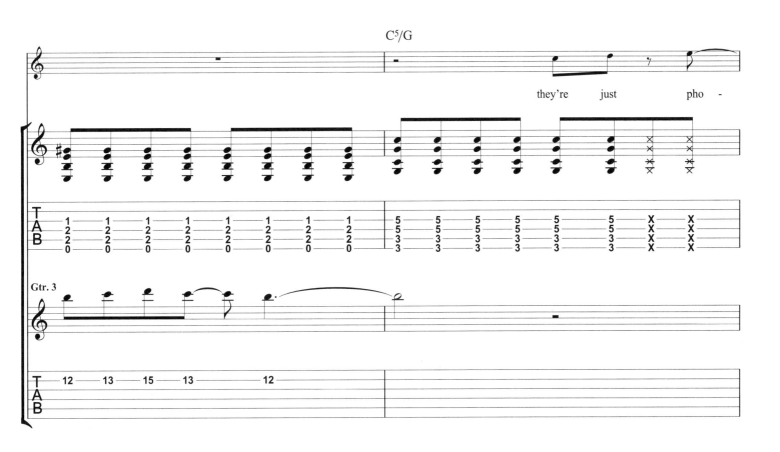

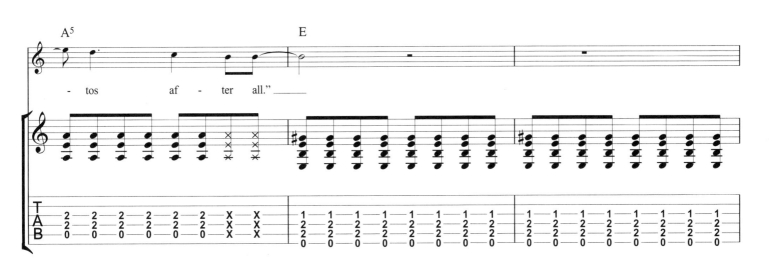

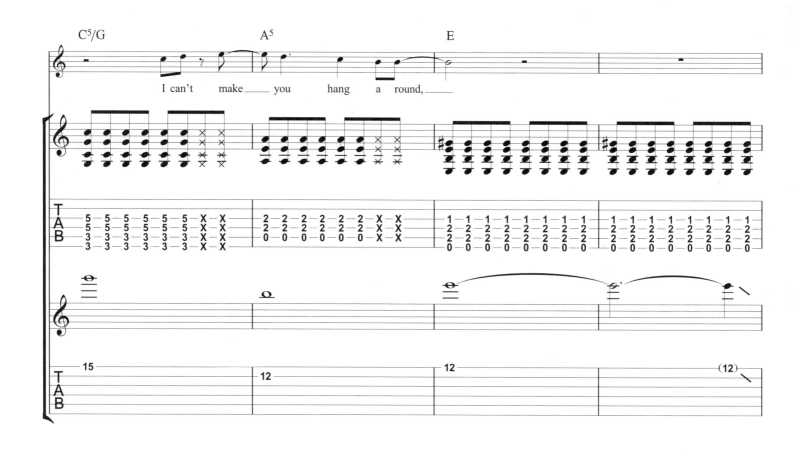

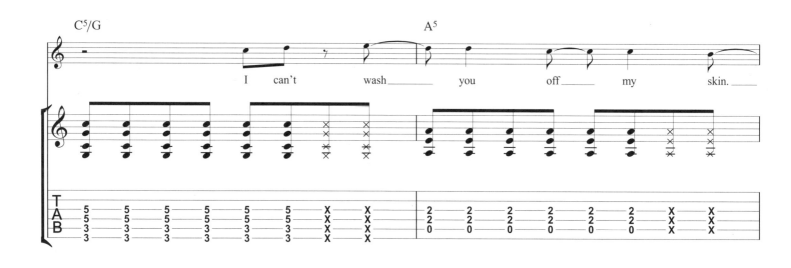

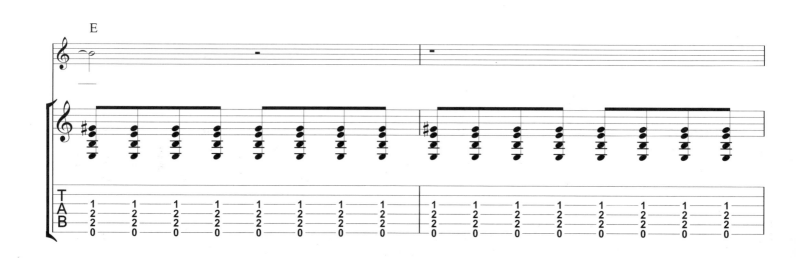

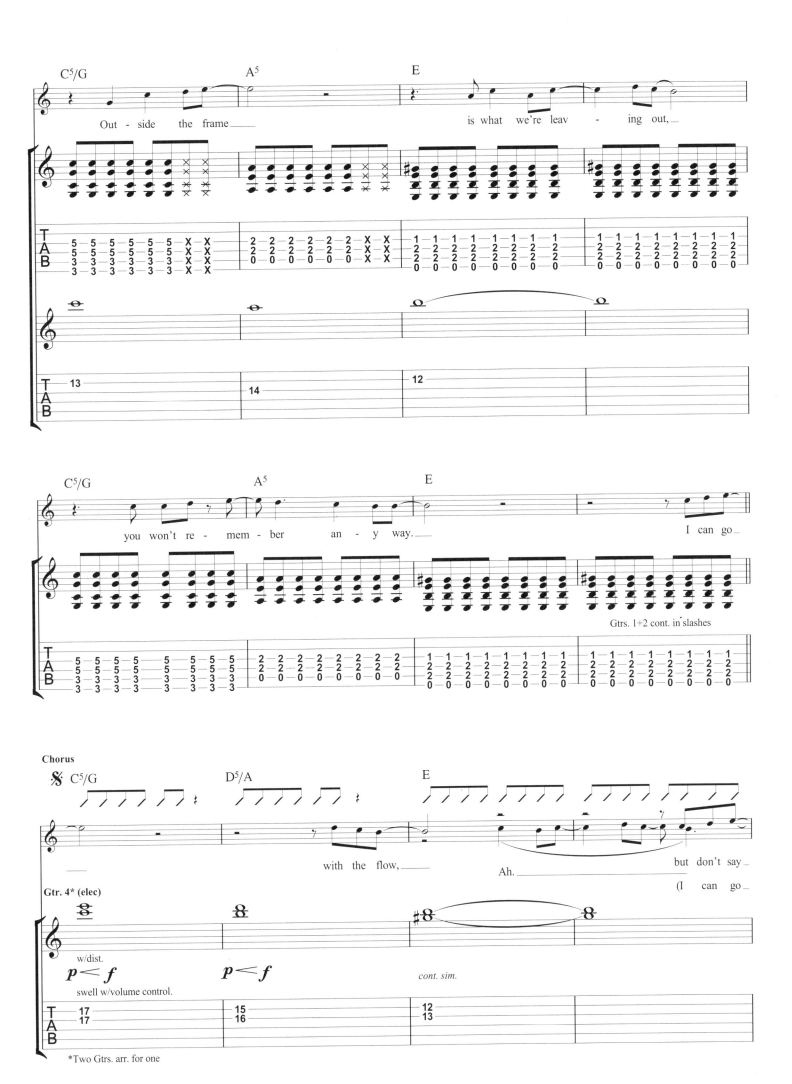

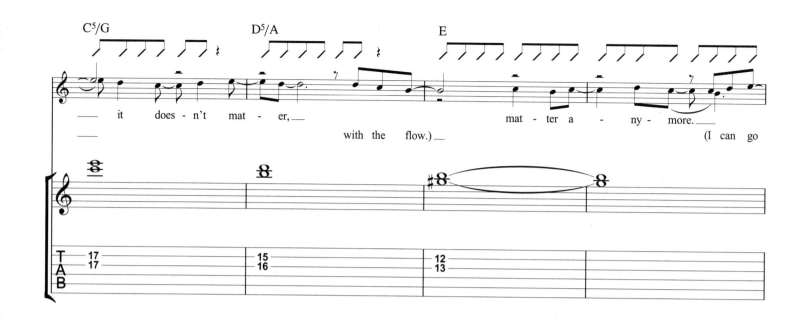

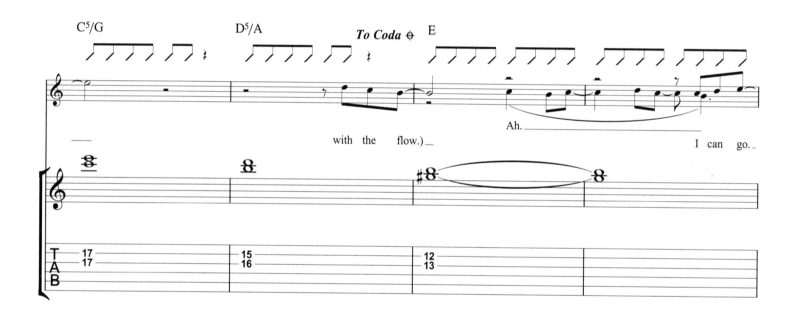

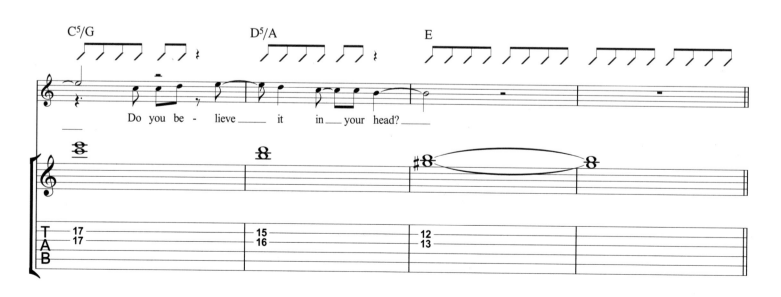

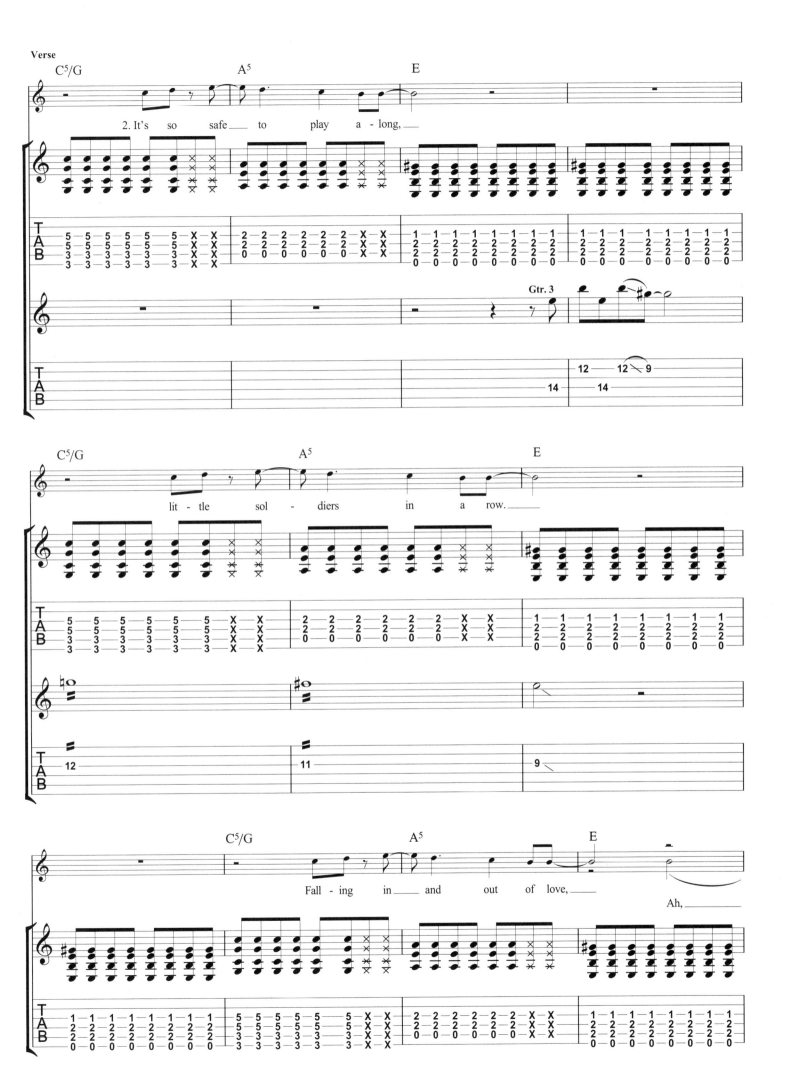

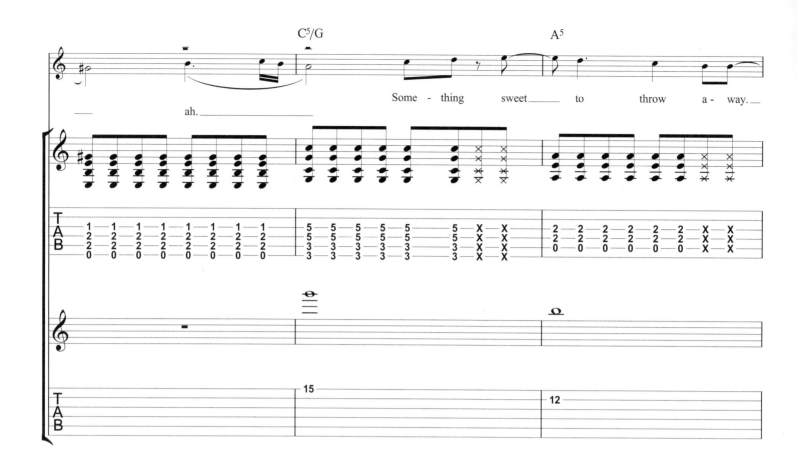

Some - thing sweet___ to throw a - way.

ah.___

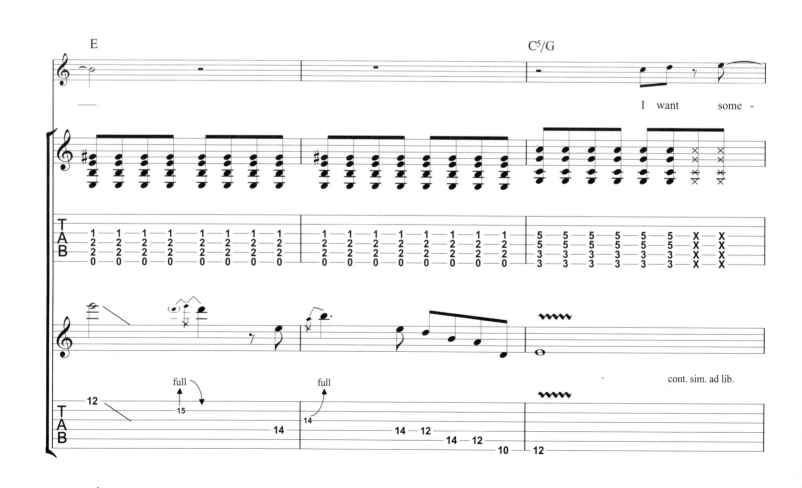

I want some -

cont. sim. ad lib.

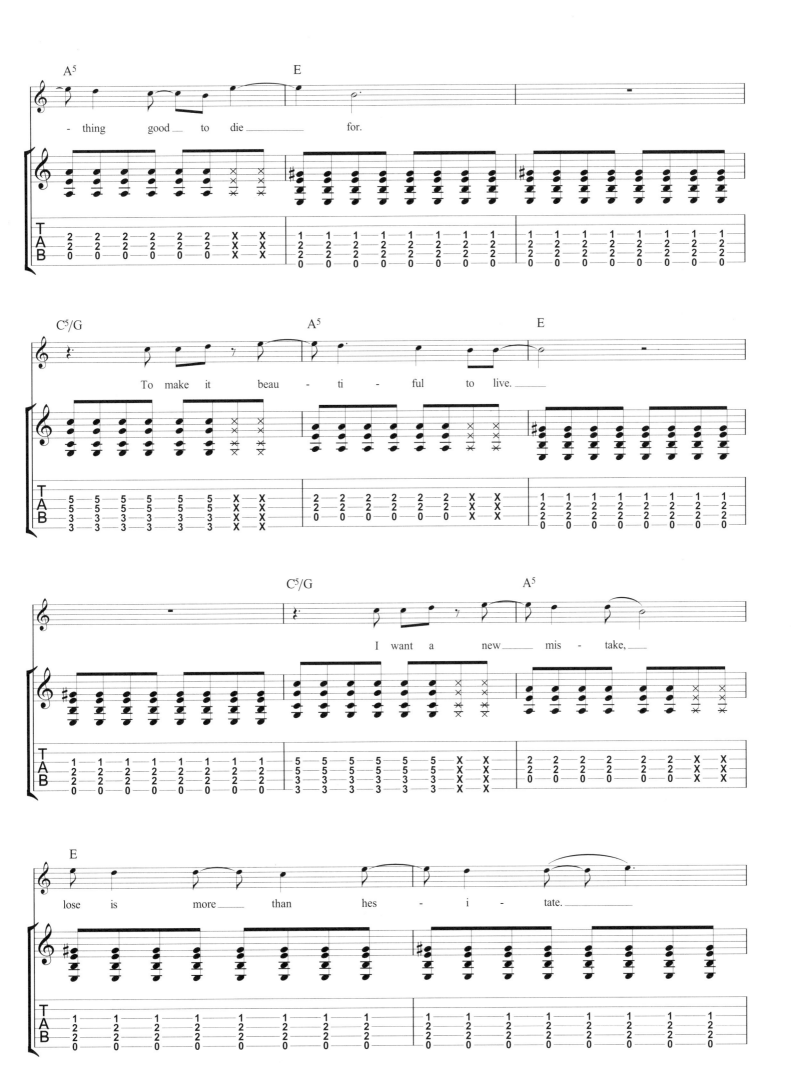

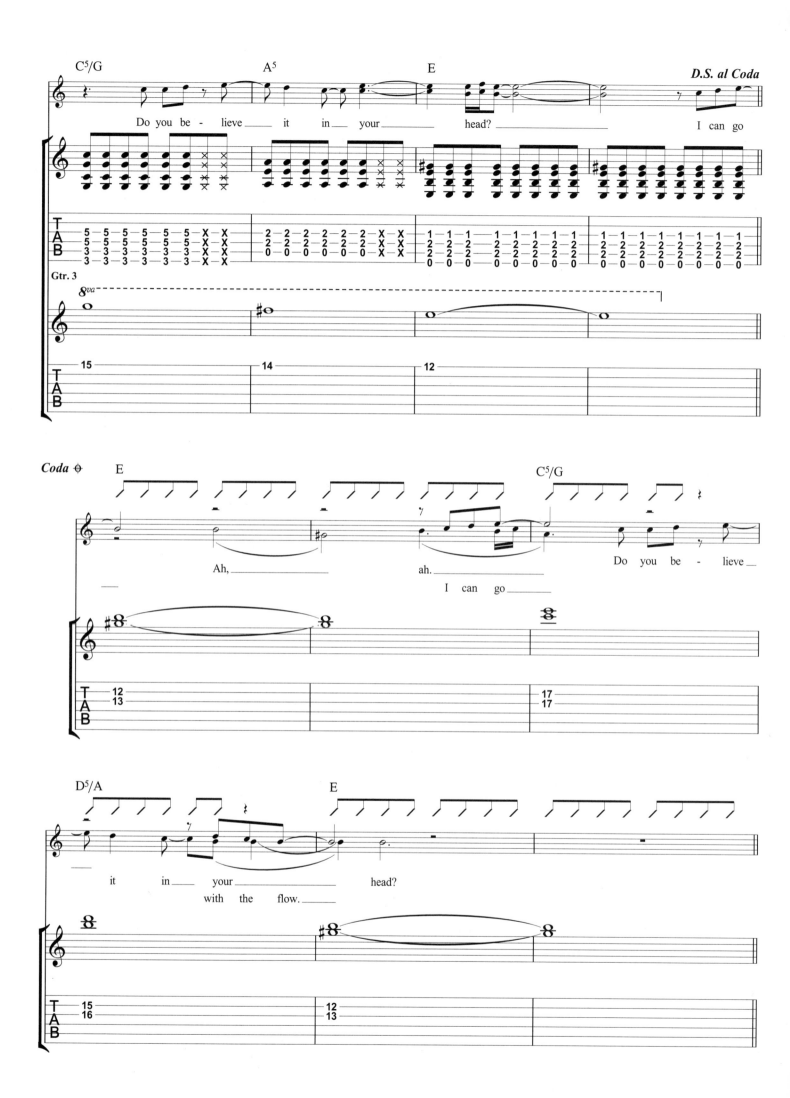

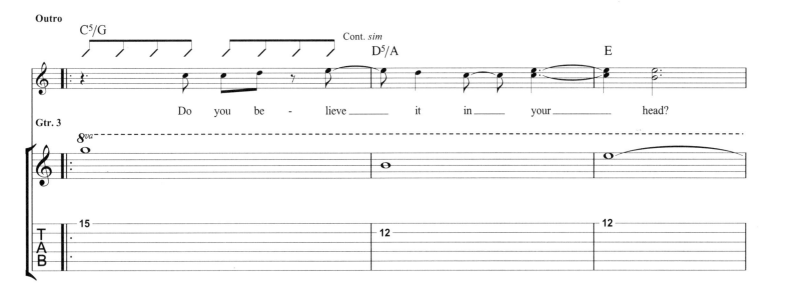

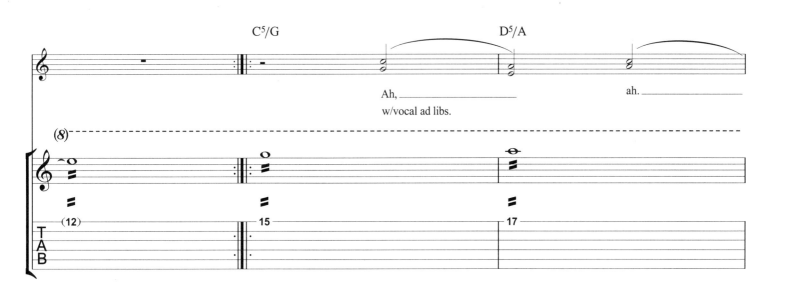

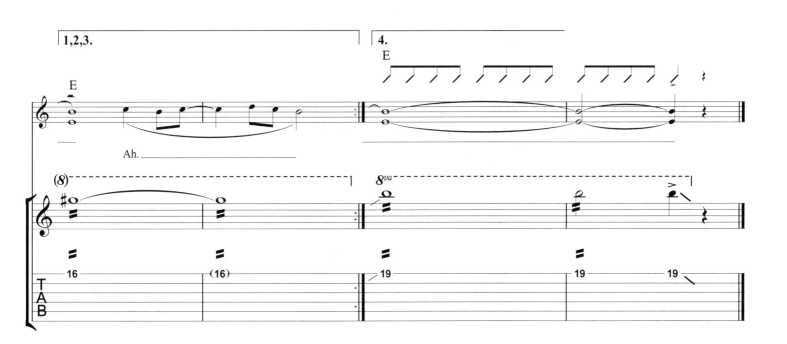

HANDS DOWN
WORDS & MUSIC BY CHRISTOPHER CARRABBA

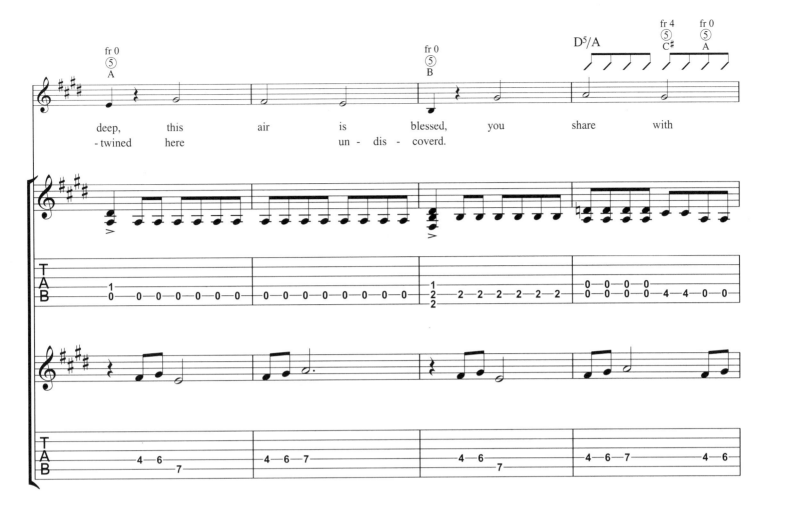

deep, this air is blessed, you share with
-twined here un - dis - coverd.

me. This night is wild, so calm and
Safe in here from all the stu - pid ques - tions; "Hey did you get

dull, these hearts they race from self con -
some?" man, that is so from dumb.

Gtr. 2 cont. sim.

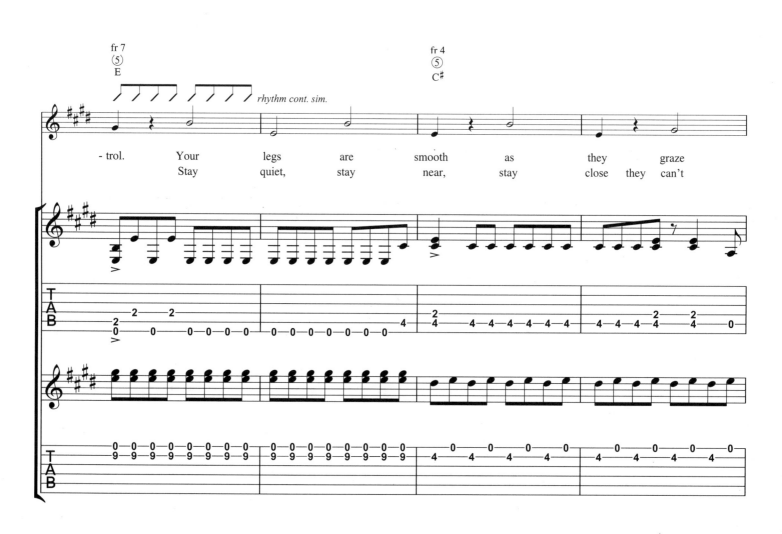

- trol. Your legs are smooth as they graze
Stay quiet, stay near, as stay close they can't

rhythm cont. sim.

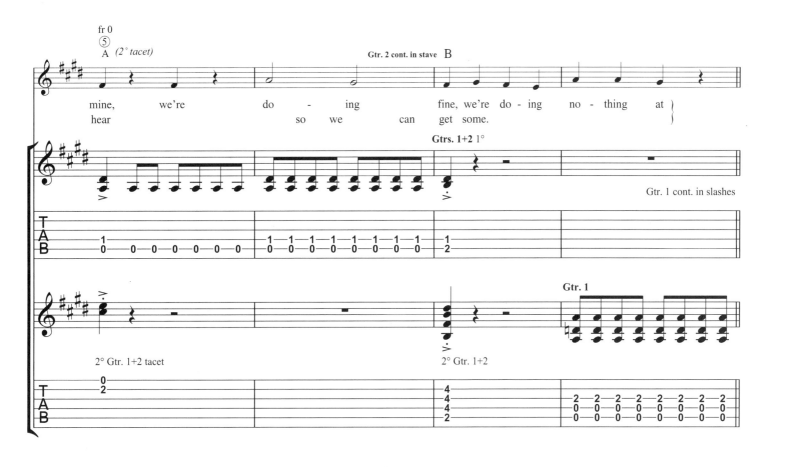

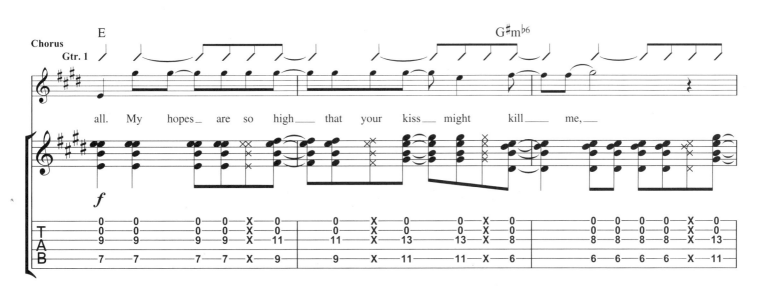

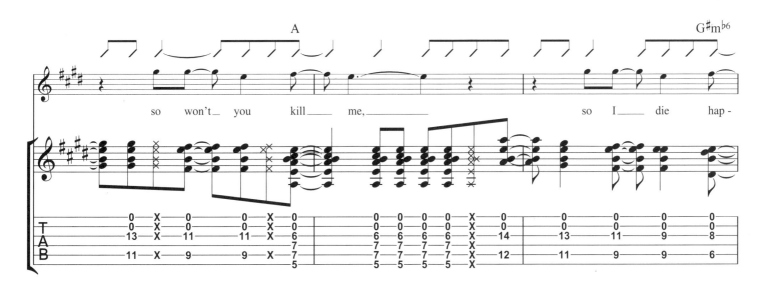

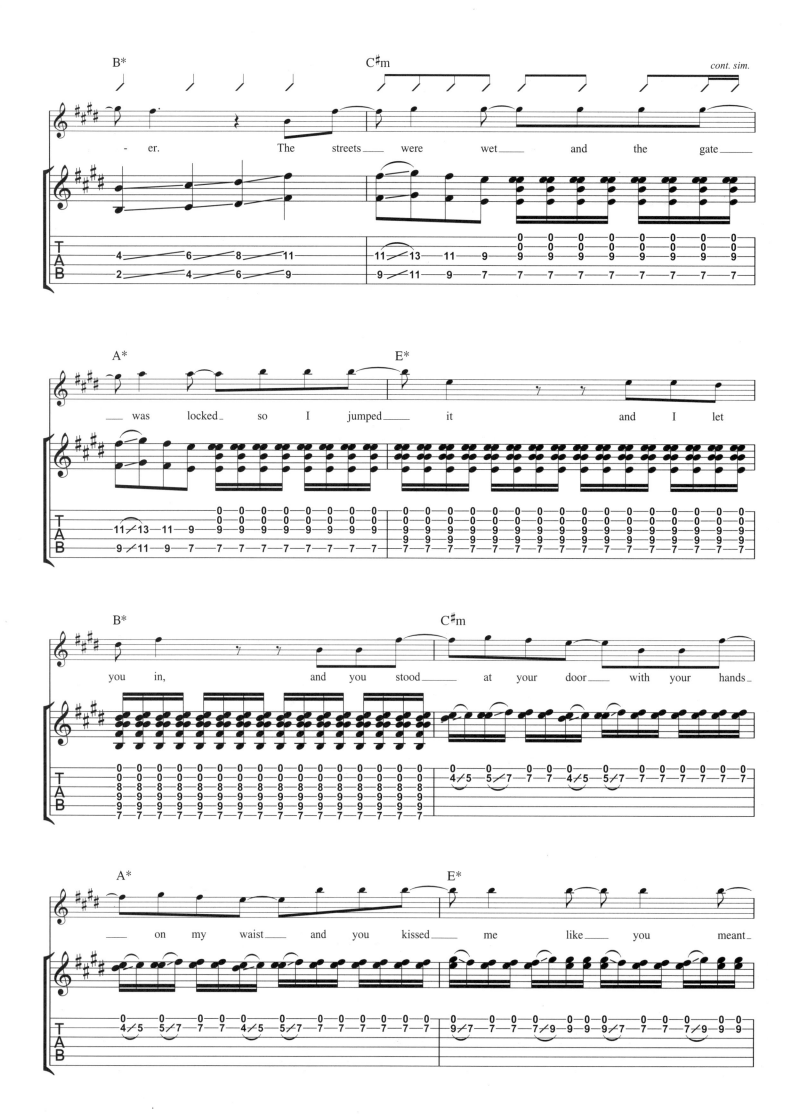

86

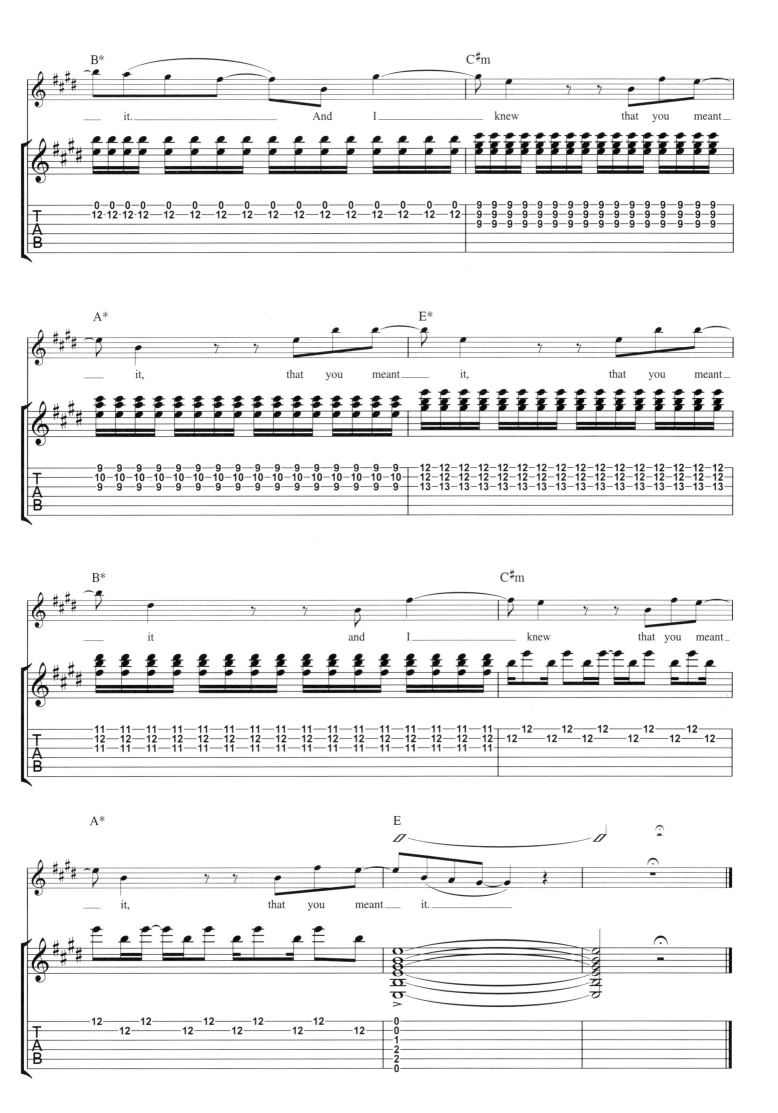

THE HINDU TIMES

WORDS & MUSIC BY NOEL GALLAGHER

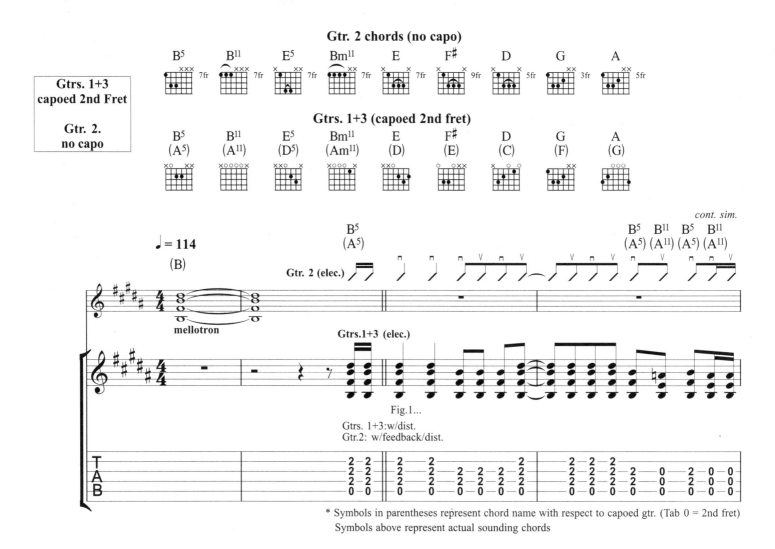

* Symbols in parentheses represent chord name with respect to capoed gtr. (Tab 0 = 2nd fret)
Symbols above represent actual sounding chords

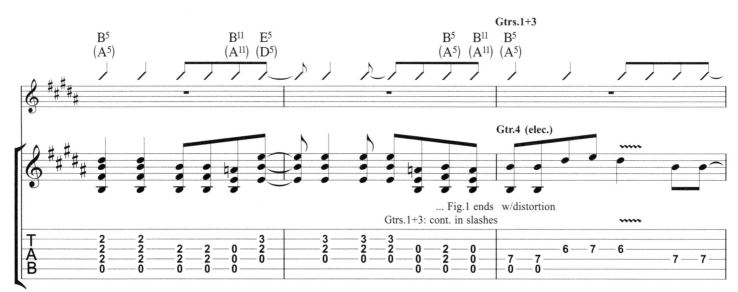

'Cos God gim-me soul ____ and all rock 'n' roll _____ (babe,) ____

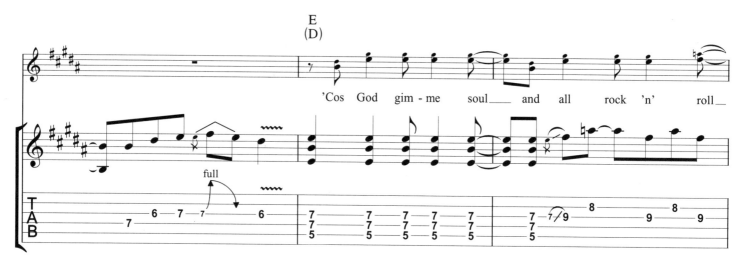

'Cos God gim-me soul ____ and all rock 'n' roll ____

_____ (babe,) ____

And I get ____

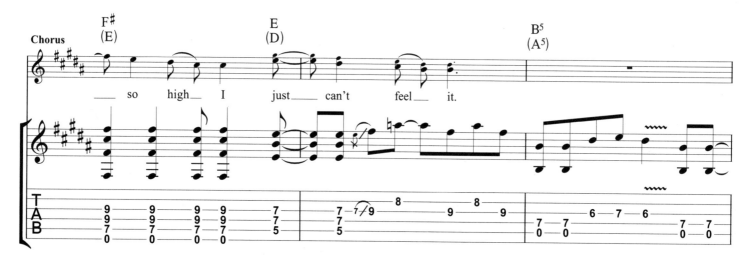

____ so high ____ I just ____ can't feel ____ it.

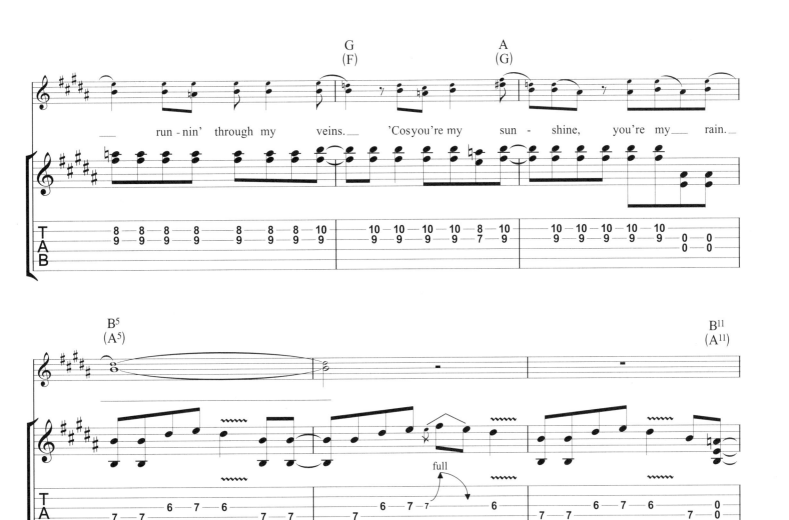

run - nin' through my veins. 'Cos you're my sun - shine, you're my rain.

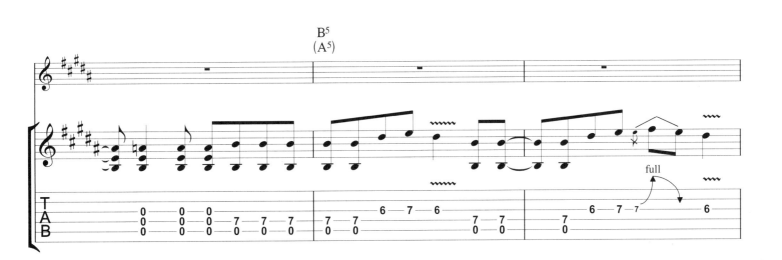

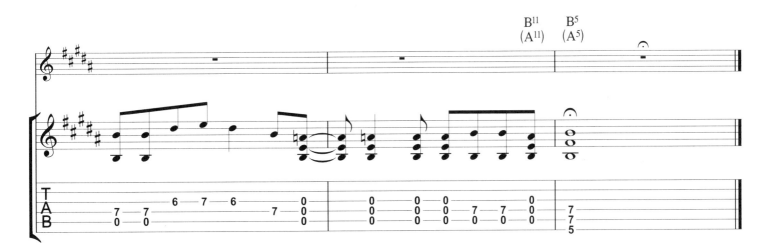

HARDER TO BREATHE

WORDS & MUSIC BY ADAM LEVINE, JAMES VALENTINE, JESSE CARMICHAEL, MICKEY MADDEN & RYAN DUSICK

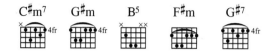

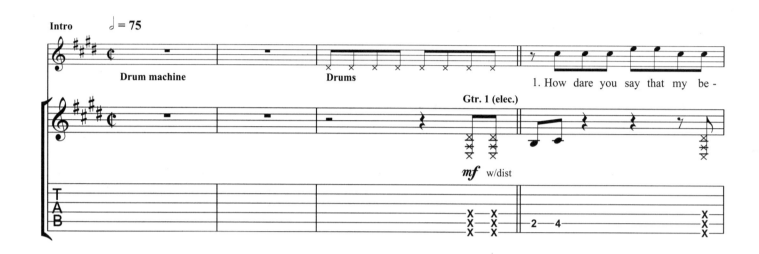

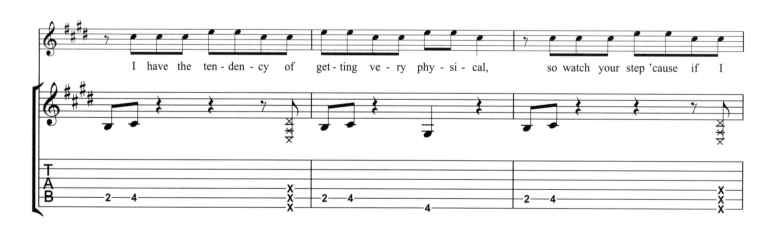

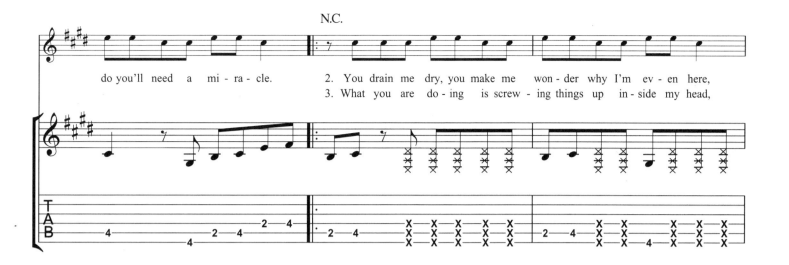

do you'll need a mi-ra-cle. 2. You drain me dry, you make me won-der why I'm ev-en here,
3. What you are do-ing is screw-ing things up in-side my head,

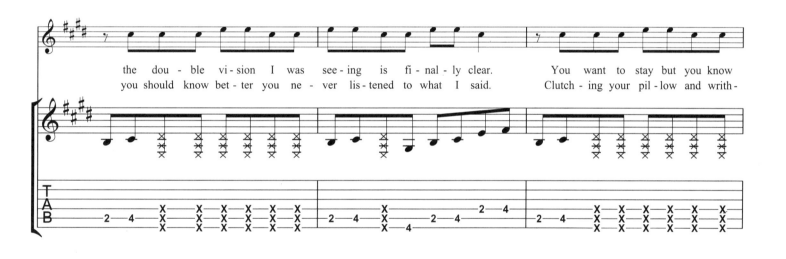

the dou-ble vi-sion I was see-ing is fi-nal-ly clear. You want to stay but you know
you should know bet-ter you ne-ver lis-tened to what I said. Clutch-ing your pil-low and writh-

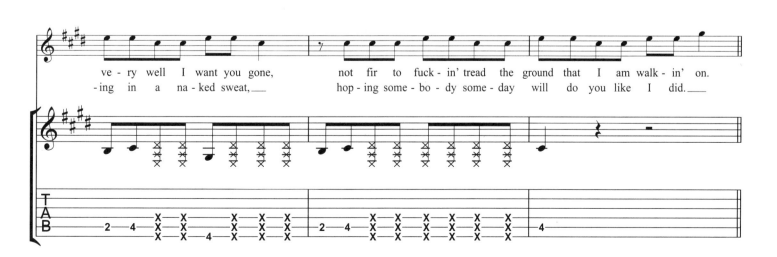

ve-ry well I want you gone, not fir to fuck-in' tread the ground that I am walk-in' on.
-ing in a na-ked sweat,___ hop-ing some-bo-dy some-day will do you like I did.___

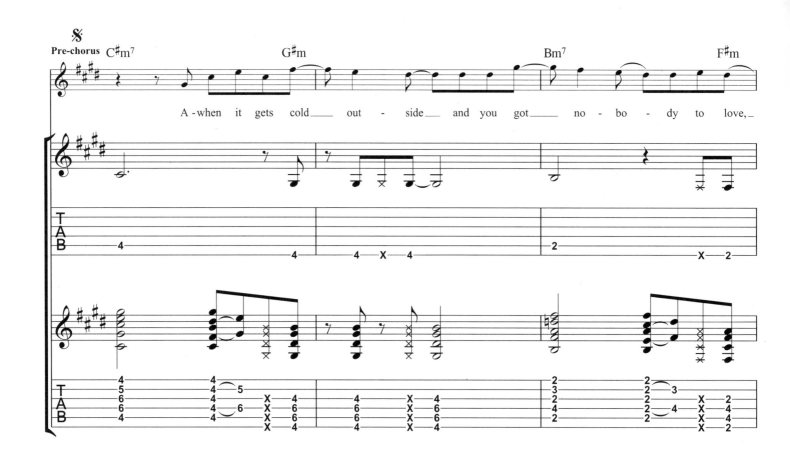

Pre-chorus

A -when it gets cold___ out - side___ and you got___ no - bo - dy to love,

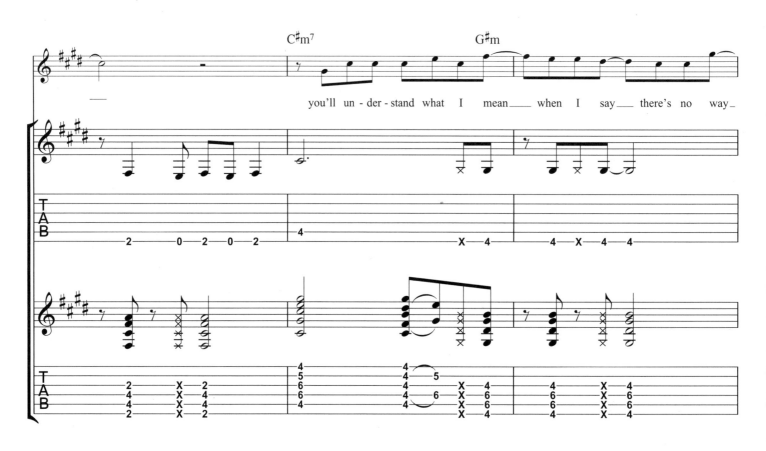

you'll un - der - stand what I mean___ when I say___ there's no way

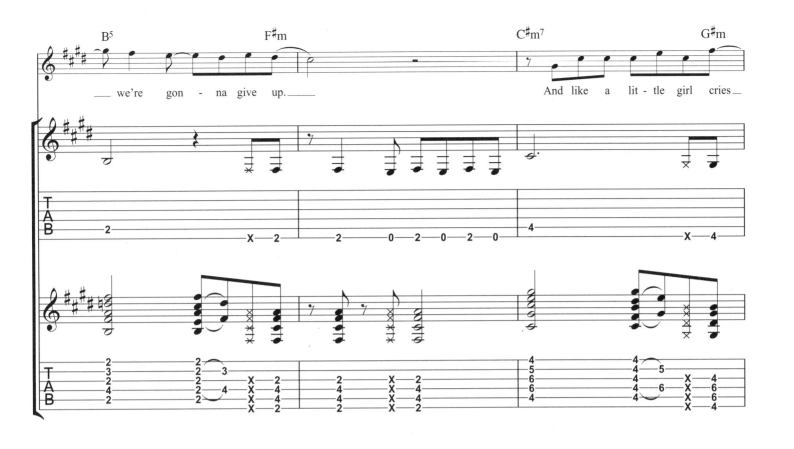

we're gon - na give up. And like a lit - tle girl cries

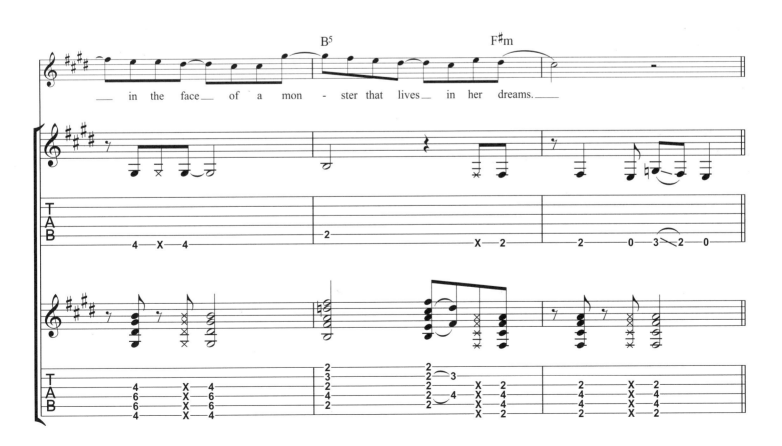

in the face of a mon - ster that lives in her dreams.

A - is there an - y - one out____ there 'cause it's get - ting hard ____ - er and hard - er to breathe?____

Is there an - y - one out____ there 'cause it's get - ting hard-

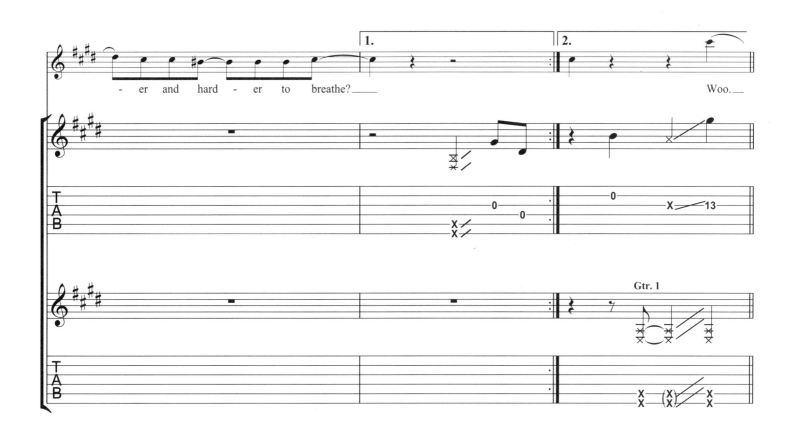

-er and hard - er to breathe?_____ Woo._____

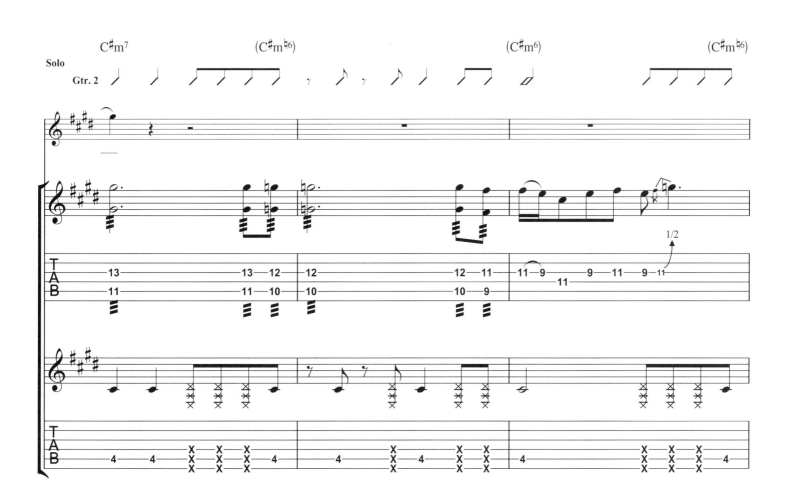

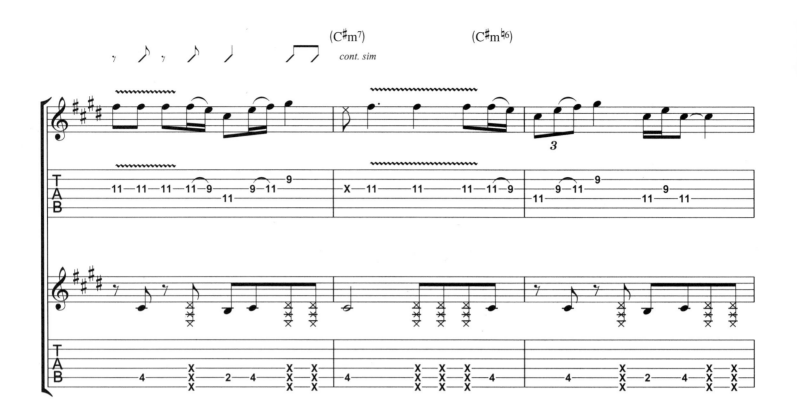

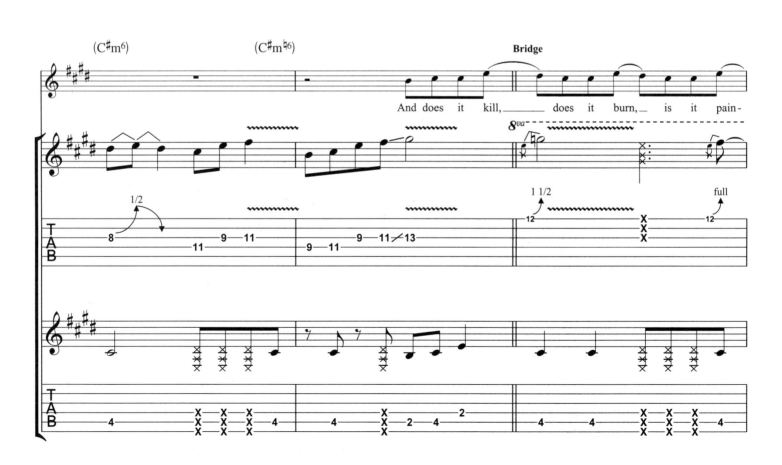

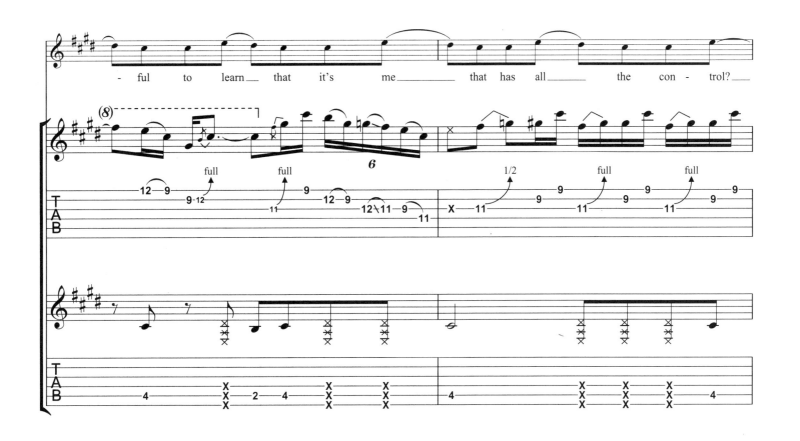

-ful   to learn___ that   it's   me_____ that has all_____ the con - trol?___

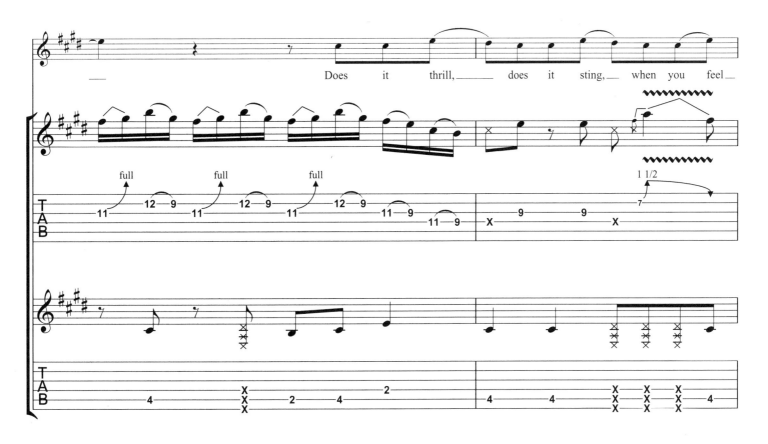

___   Does it   thrill,_____ does it sting,___ when you feel___

Coda

I JUST DON'T KNOW WHAT TO DO WITH MYSELF

WORDS BY HAL DAVID
MUSIC BY BURT BACHARACH

I MISS YOU

WORDS & MUSIC BY MARK HOPPUS, TOM DELONGE & TRAVIS BARKER

Original Key: B Major (tune down a minor 3rd)

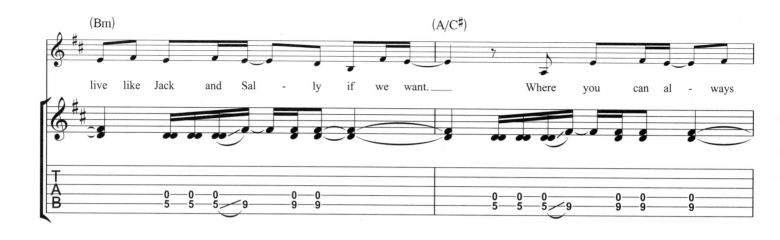

live like Jack and Sal - ly if we want.___ Where you can al - ways

find me, and we'll have Hal - low - een___ on Christ - mas. And

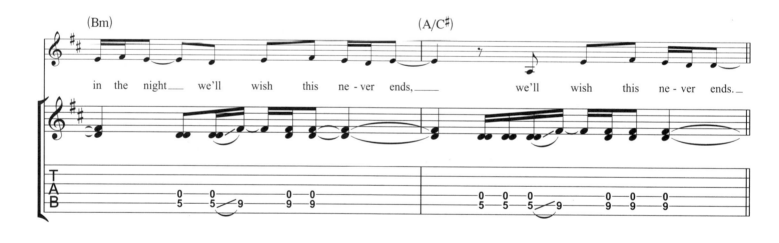

in the night___ we'll wish this ne - ver ends,___ we'll wish this ne - ver ends.___

Chorus

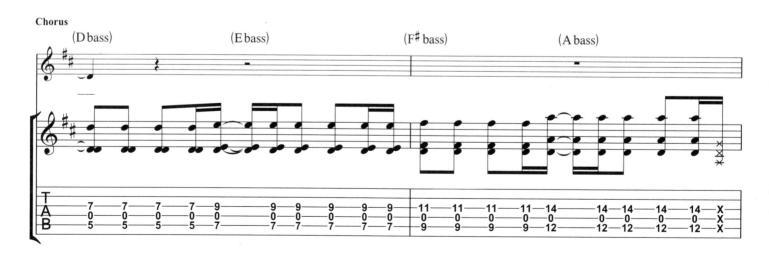

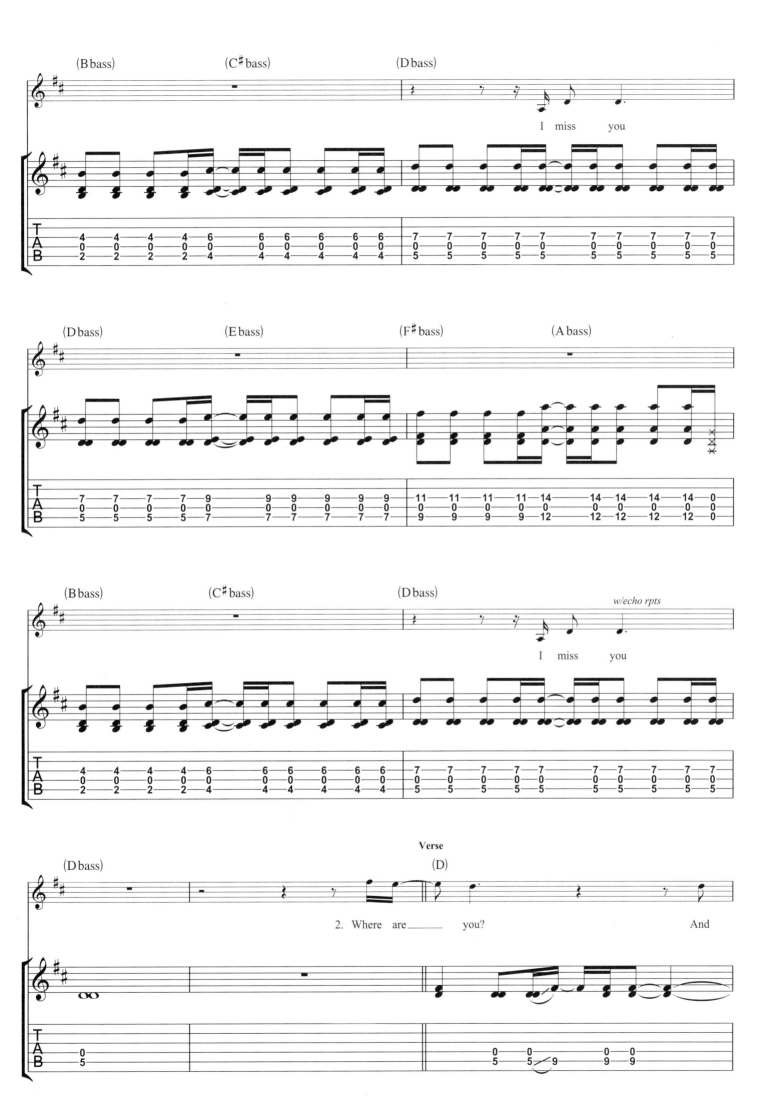

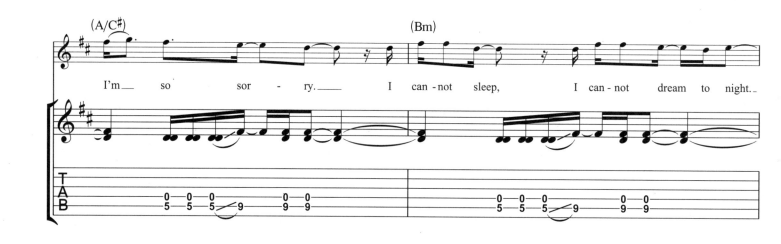

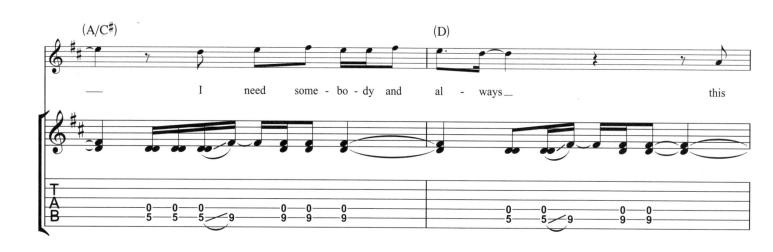

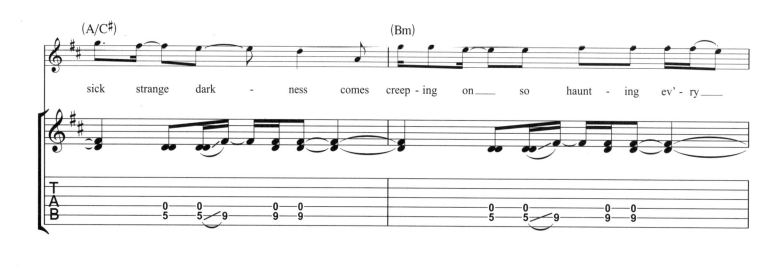

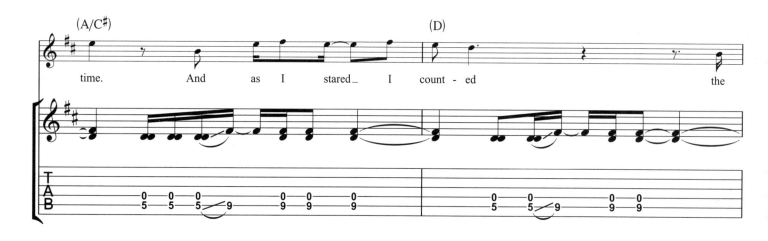

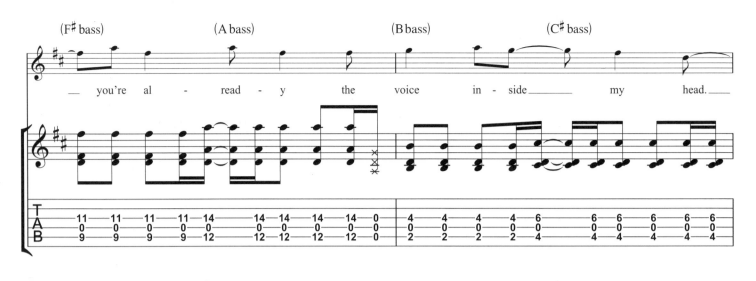

(F# bass)　(A bass)　(B bass)　(C# bass)

＿ you're al - read - y the voice in - side＿ my head.＿

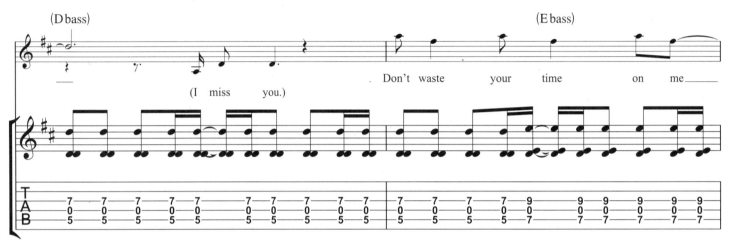

(D bass)　(E bass)

＿ (I miss you.)

Don't waste your time on me＿

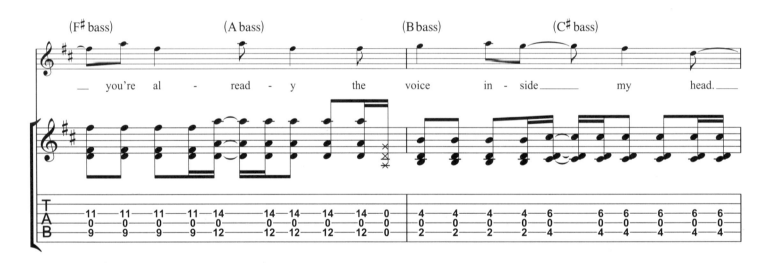

(F# bass)　(A bass)　(B bass)　(C# bass)

＿ you're al - read - y the voice in - side＿ my head.＿

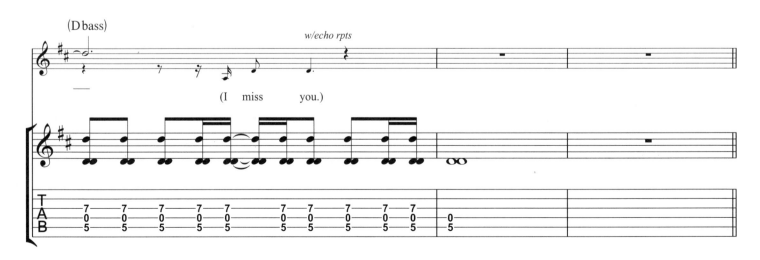

(D bass)

w/echo rpts

＿ (I miss you.)

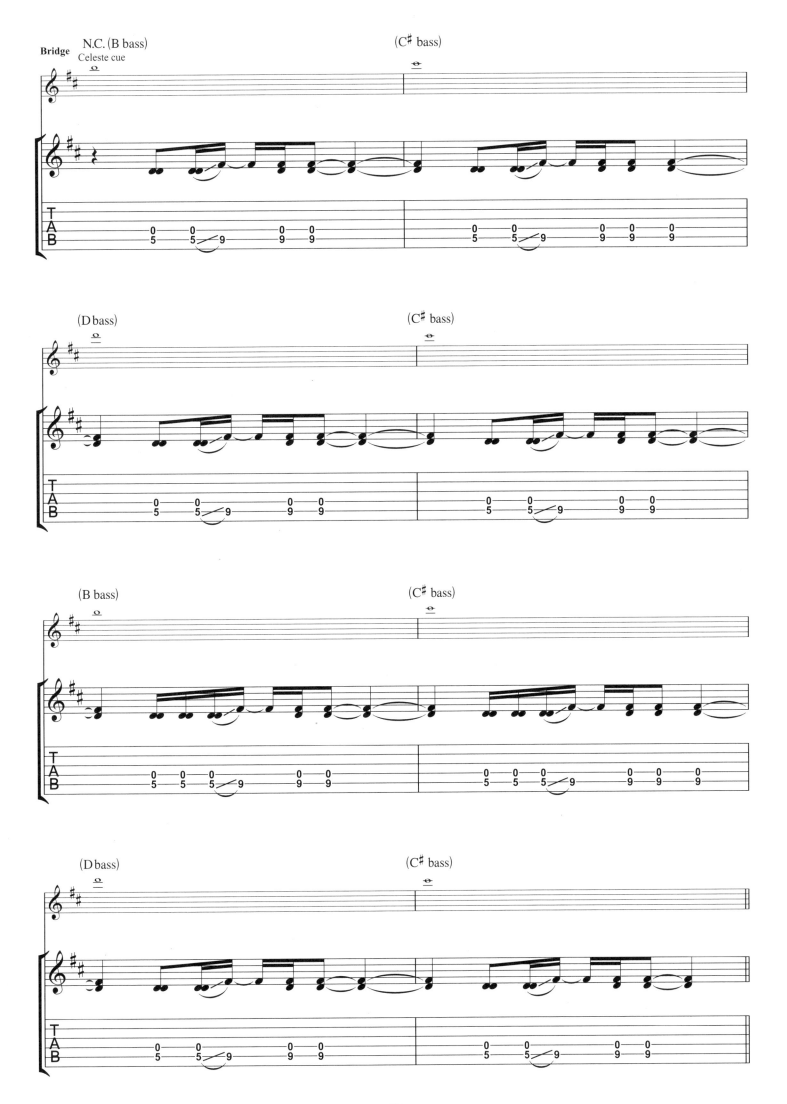

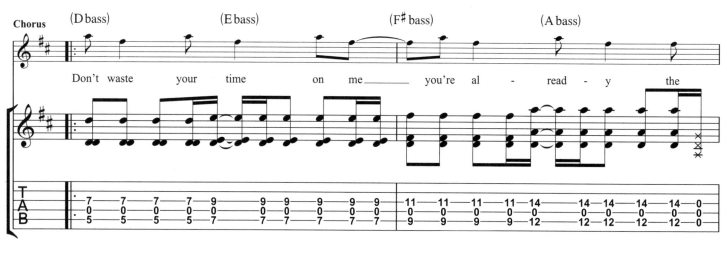

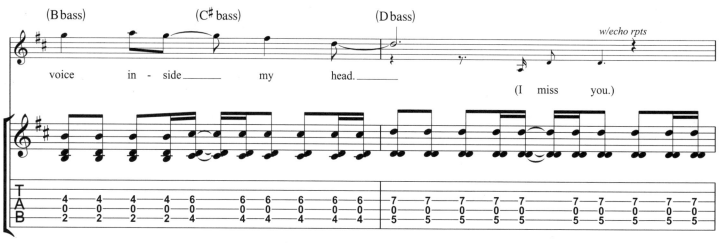

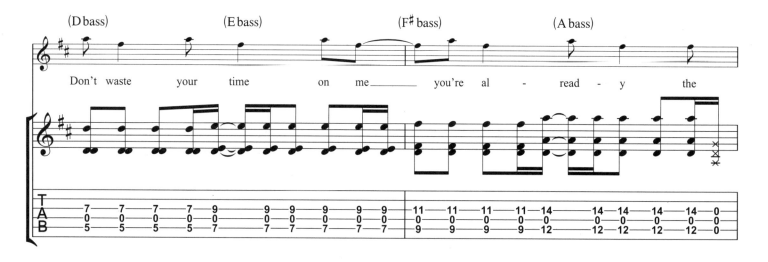

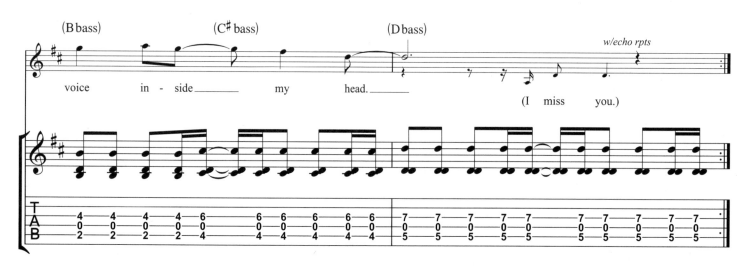

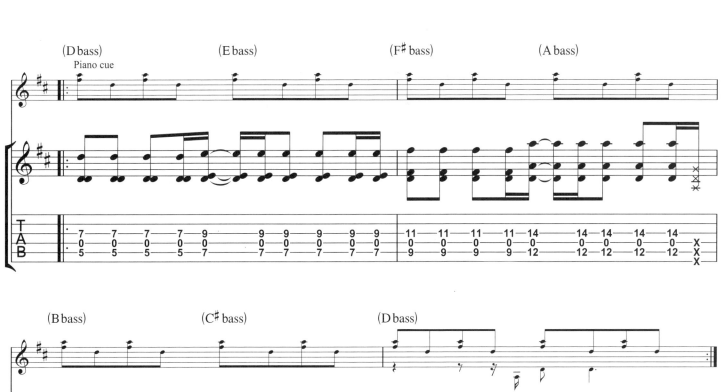

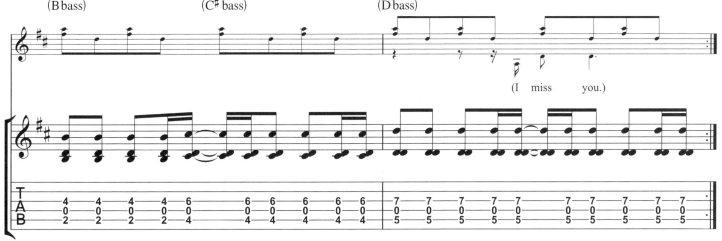

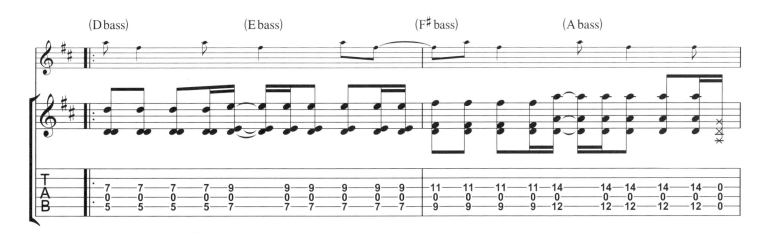

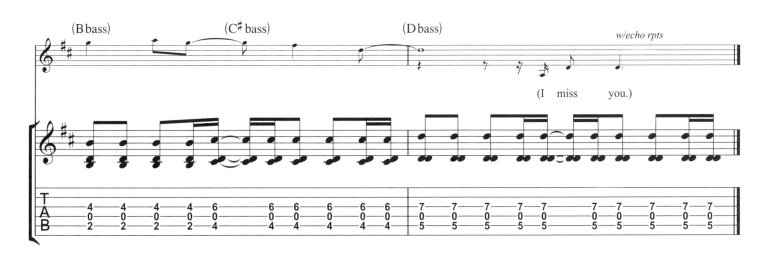

Maybe Tomorrow

WORDS & MUSIC BY KELLY JONES, RICHARD JONES & STUART CABLE

*optional piano arr. for Gtr. 4

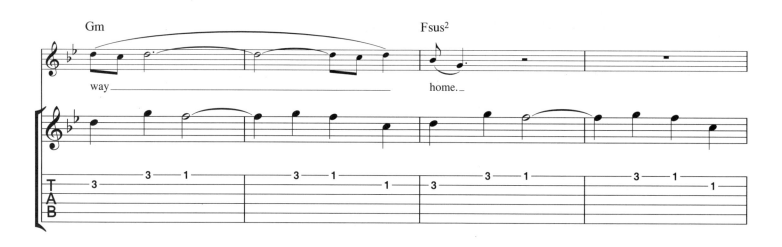

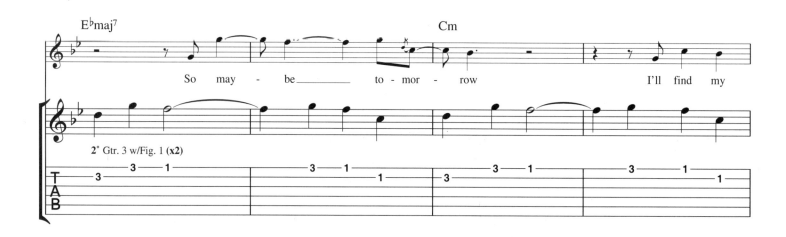

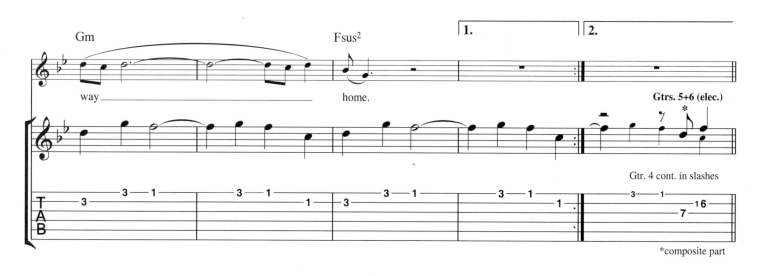

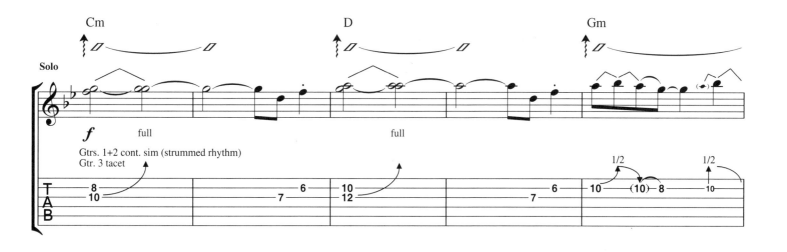

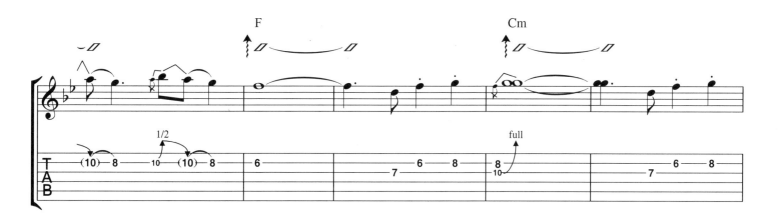

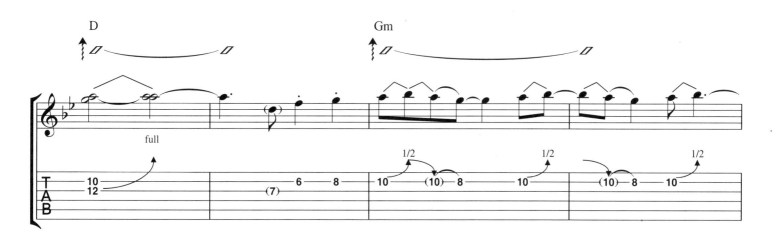

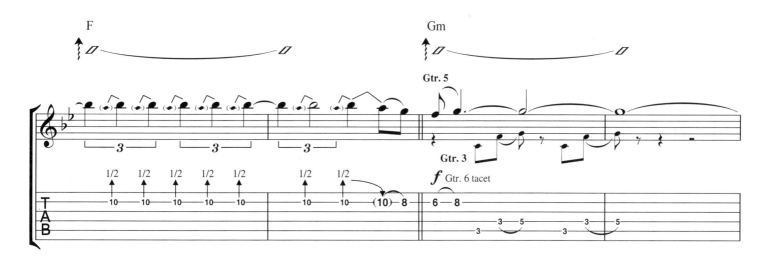

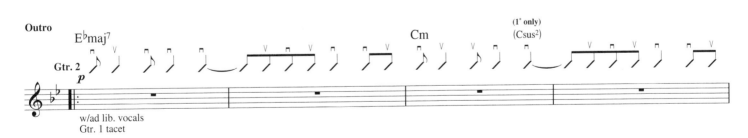

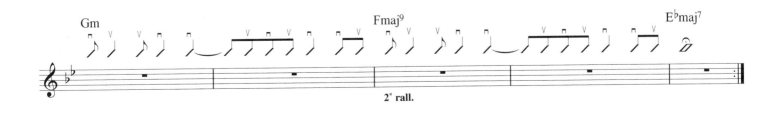

Numb

Words & Music by Chester Bennington, Mike Shinoda, Rob Bourdon, Joseph Hahn, Brad Delson & David Farrell

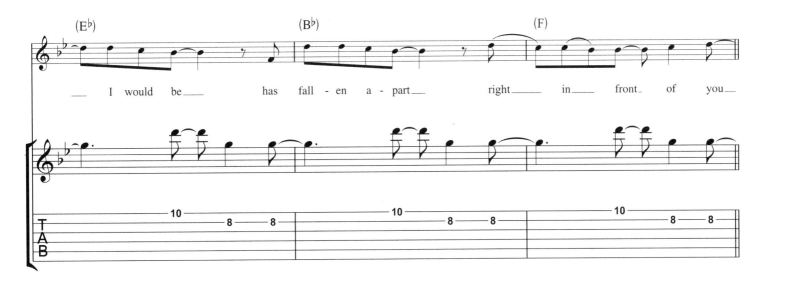

Pre-chorus

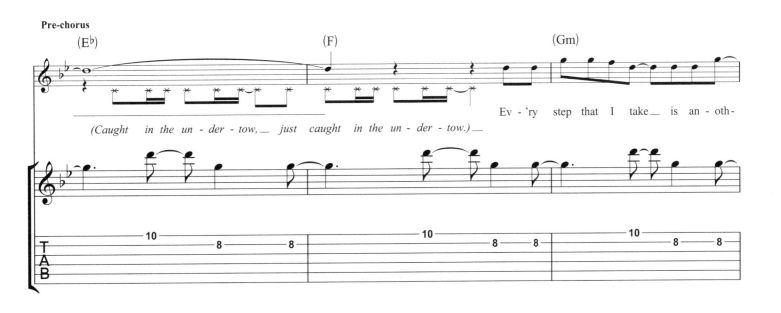

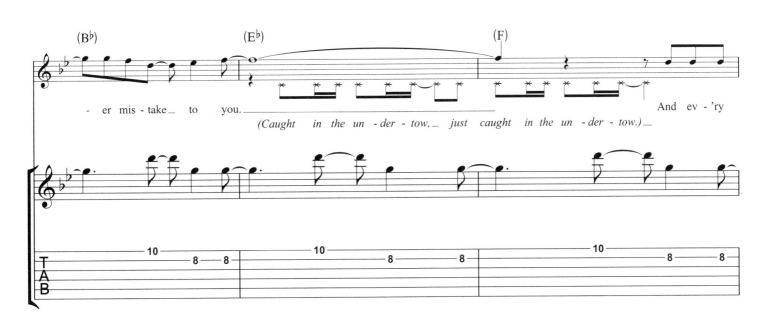

IN THE SHADOWS

WORDS & MUSIC BY LAURI YLONEN, EERO HEINONEN, AKI HAKALA & PAULI RANTASALMI

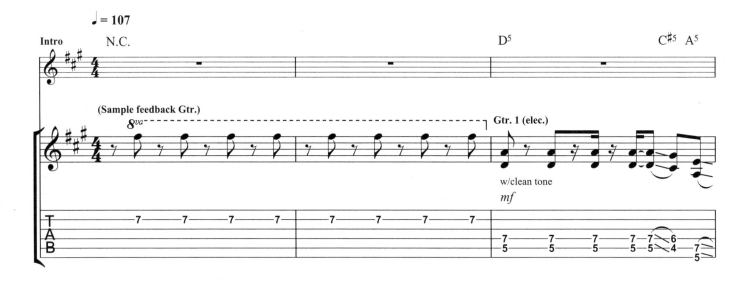

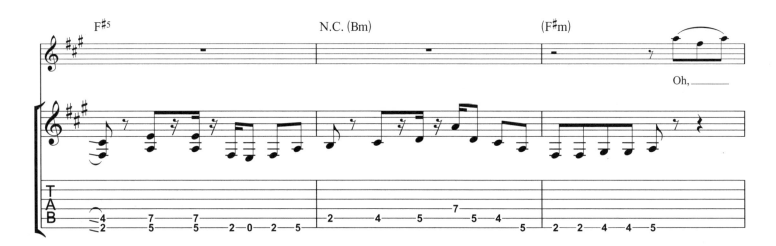

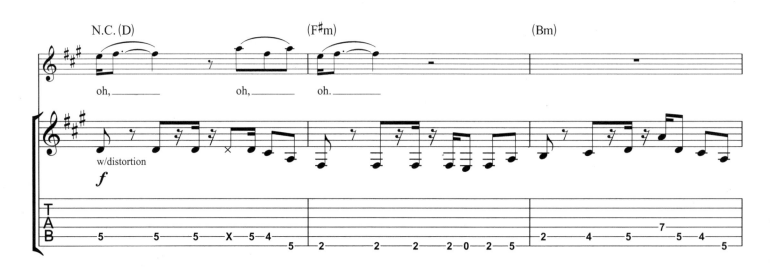

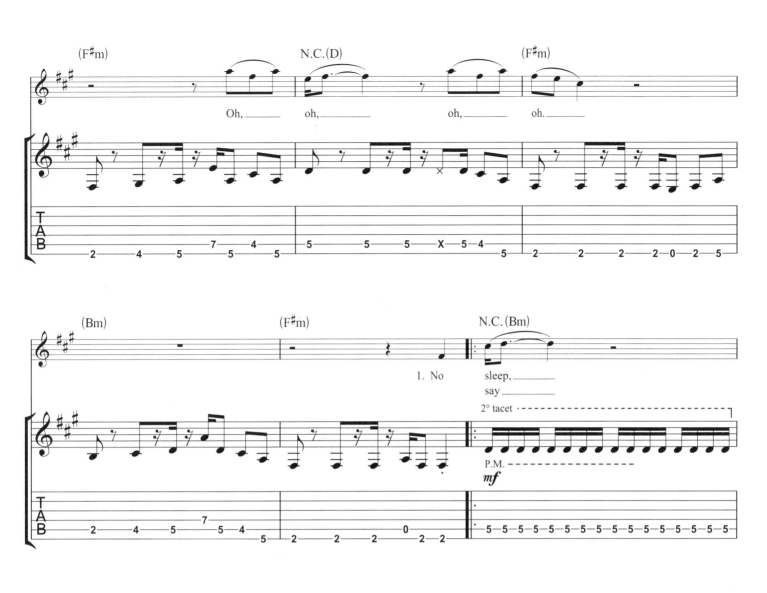

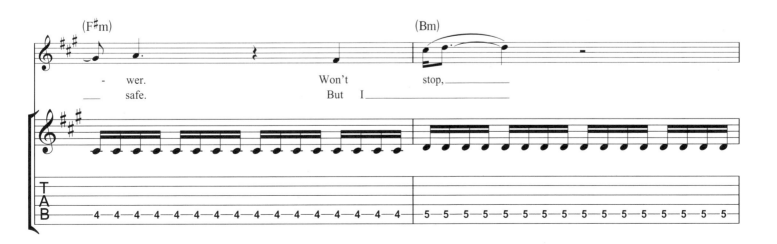

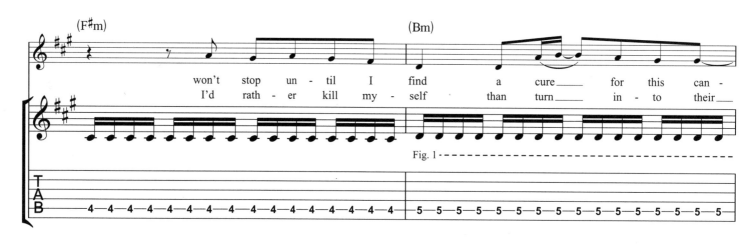

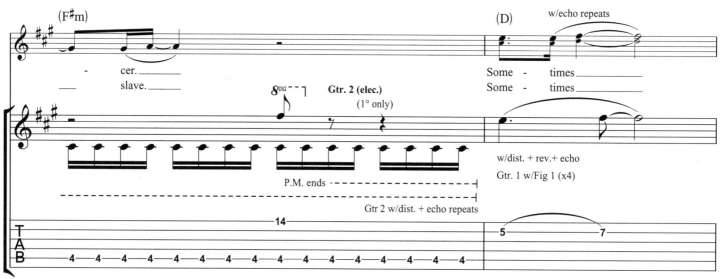

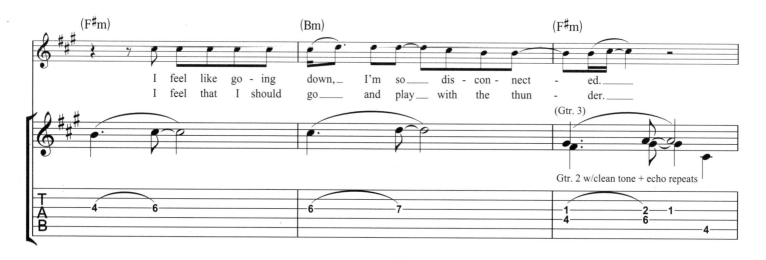

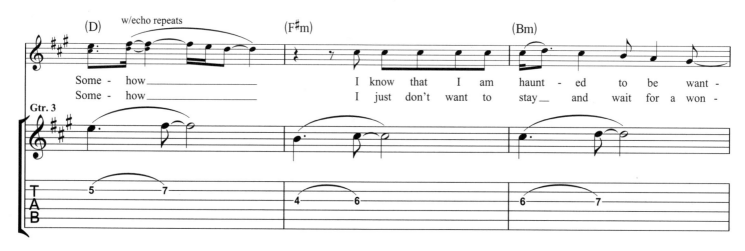

RE-OFFENDER

WORDS & MUSIC BY FRAN HEALY

Bm   Asus²   Em   G

♩ = 94

Intro   N.C.   (Bm)   (Asus²)

Drums   Gtr. 1 (acous.)

mp

(Em)   (Asus²)   Verse

Bm   cont. sim.

Gtr. 3 (2° only)

1. Keep - ing up__ ap - pear - an - ces,_____
2. Ev - 'ry - bo - dy thinks you're well,_____

2° w/Gtr. 2

Asus²   Em   Asus²

keep - ing up__ with the Jones - es._____
ev - 'ry - bo - dy thinks I'm__ ill._____

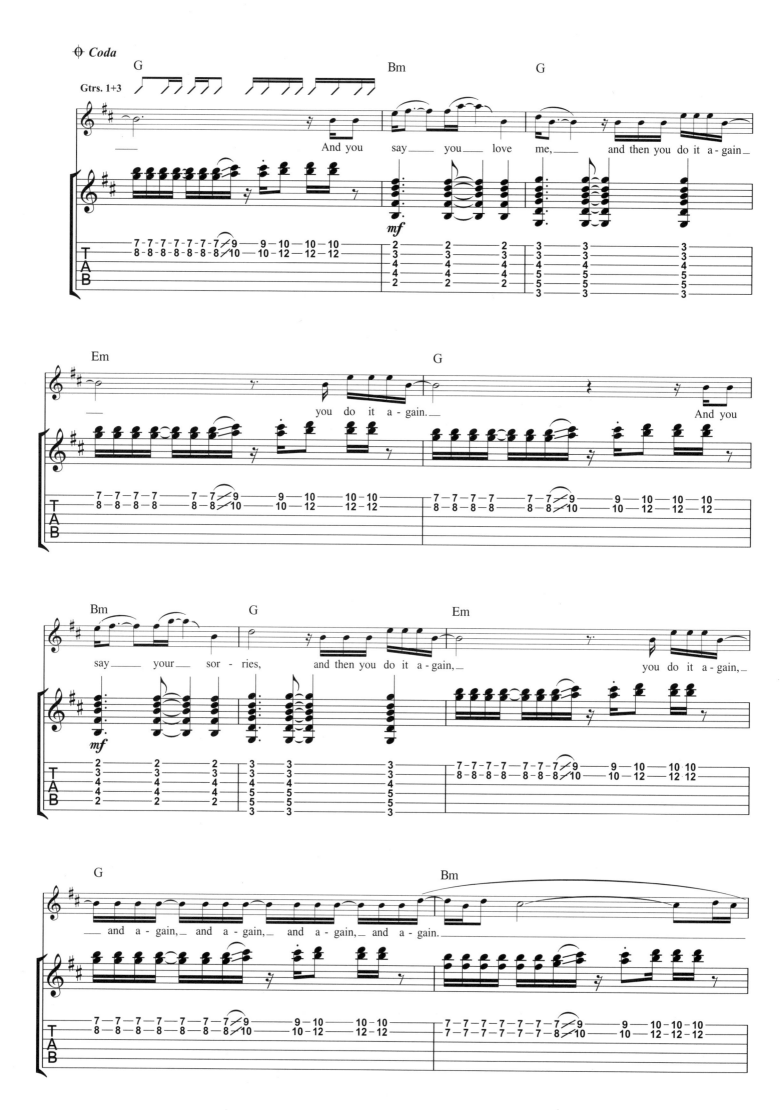

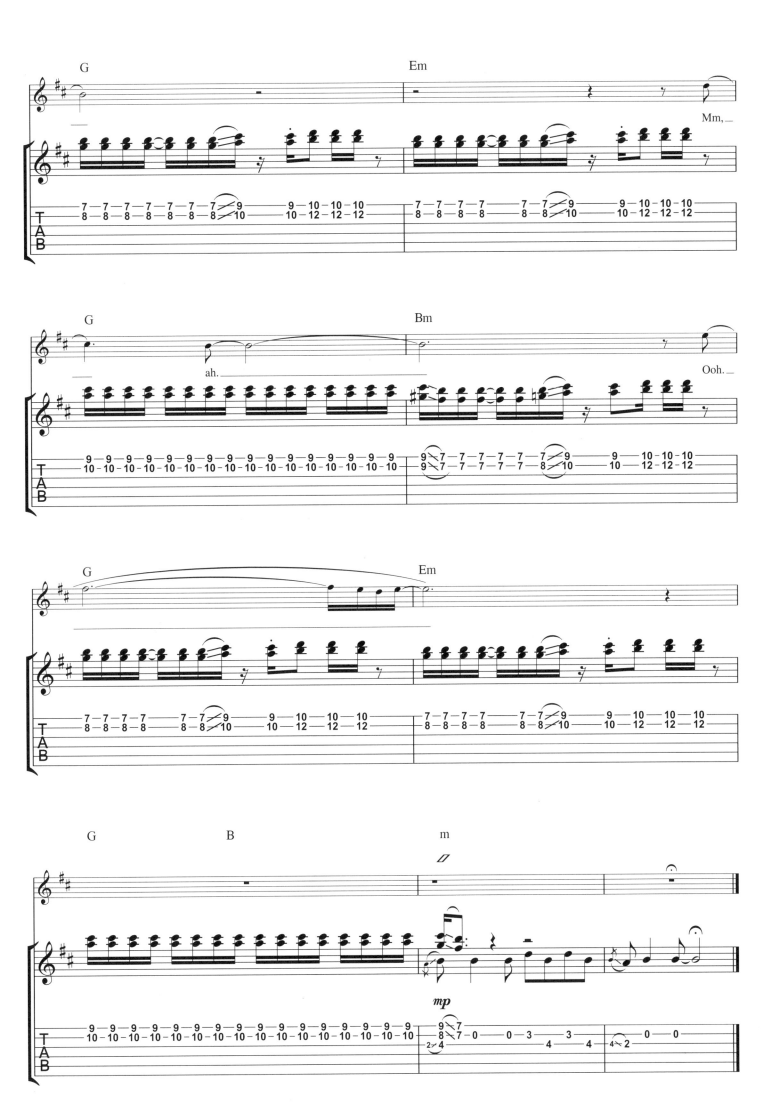

RUN

WORDS & MUSIC BY GARY LIGHTBODY, JONATHAN QUINN, MARK McCLELLAND, NATHAN CONNOLLY & IAIN ARCHER

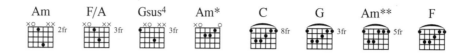

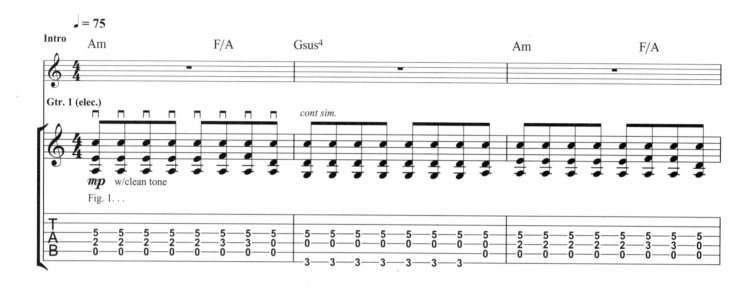

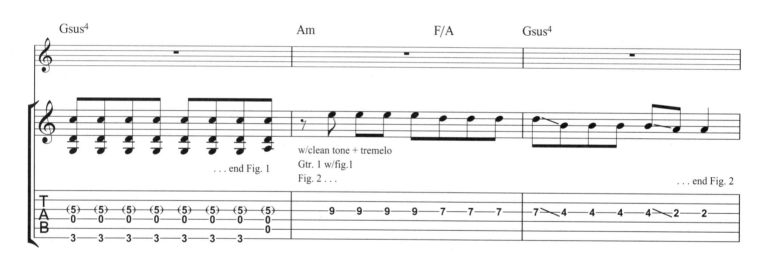

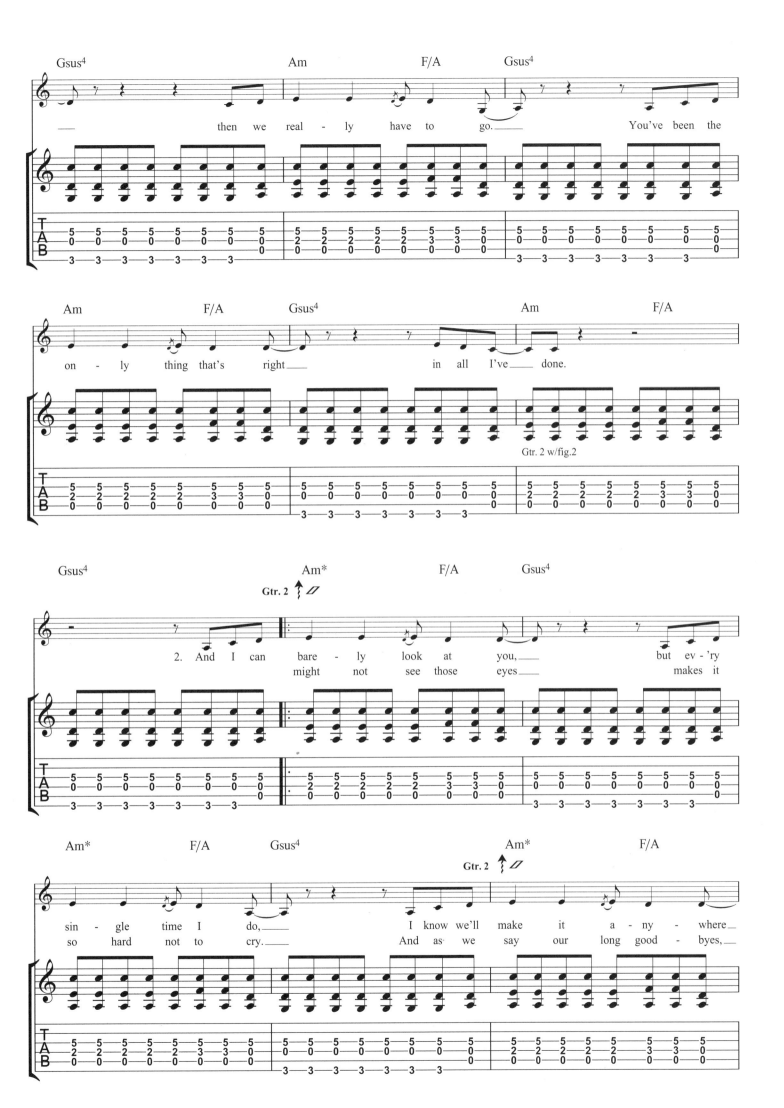

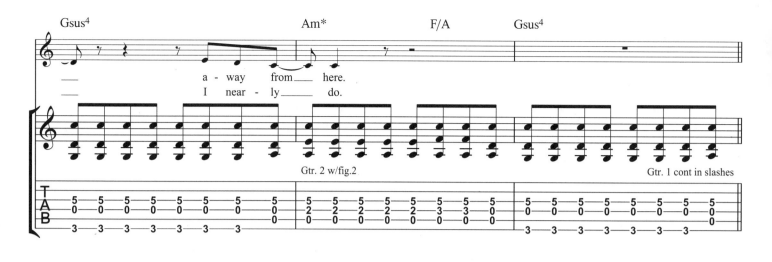

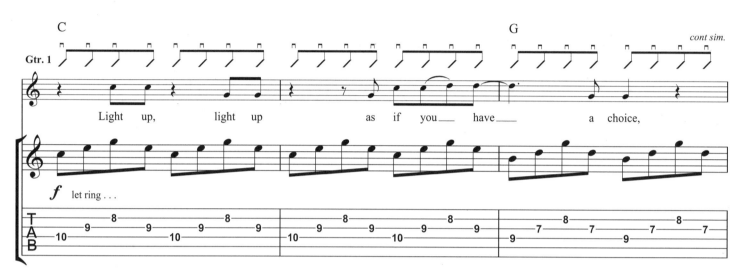

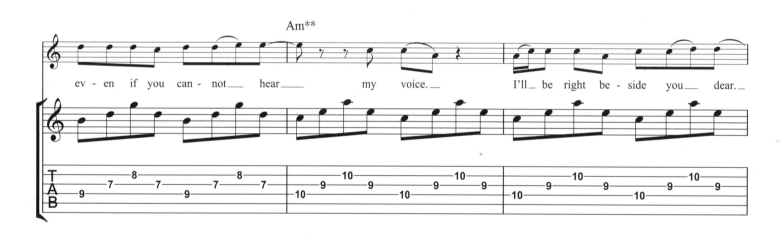

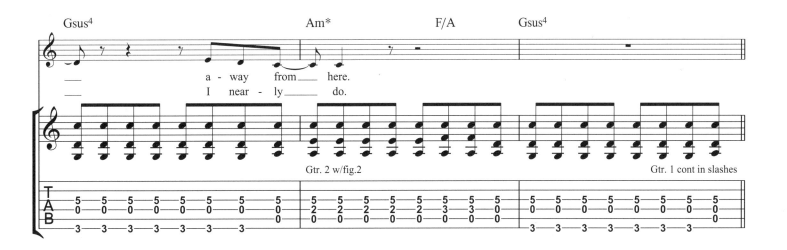

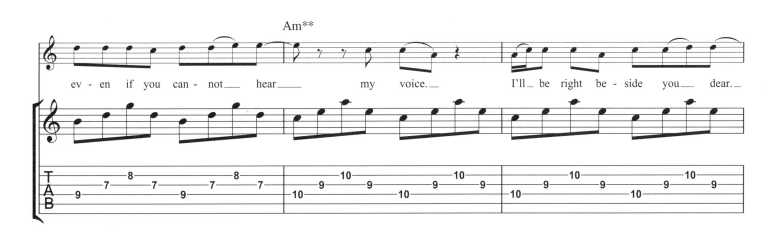

we don't have___ time___ for that. All I want's to find an___ eas-
we're bound to___ be___ a - fraid, ev - en if it's just for___ a

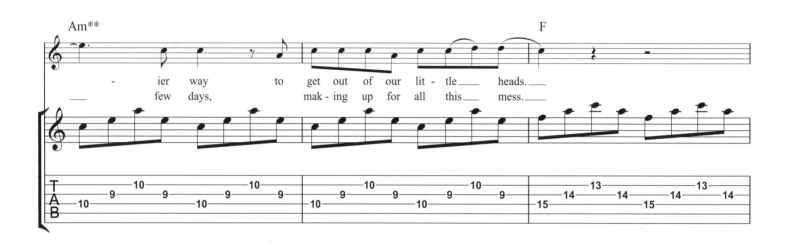

- ier way to get out of our lit - tle___ heads.___
___ few days, mak - ing up for all this___ mess.___

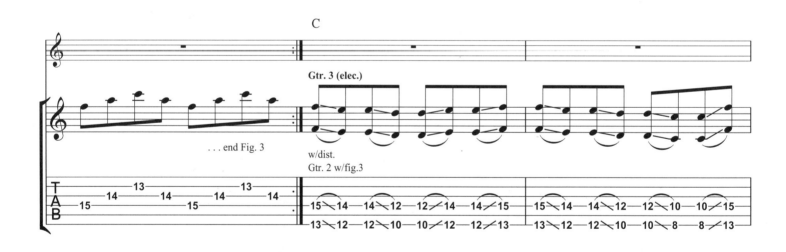

. . . end Fig. 3

Gtr. 3 (elec.)
w/dist.
Gtr. 2 w/fig.3

Light up, light up, as if you__ have a choice, ev-en if you can-not__ hear__ my voice,__ I'll be right be-side you dear.__

Stacy's Mom

WORDS & MUSIC BY ADAM SCHLESINGER & CHRIS COLLINGWOOD

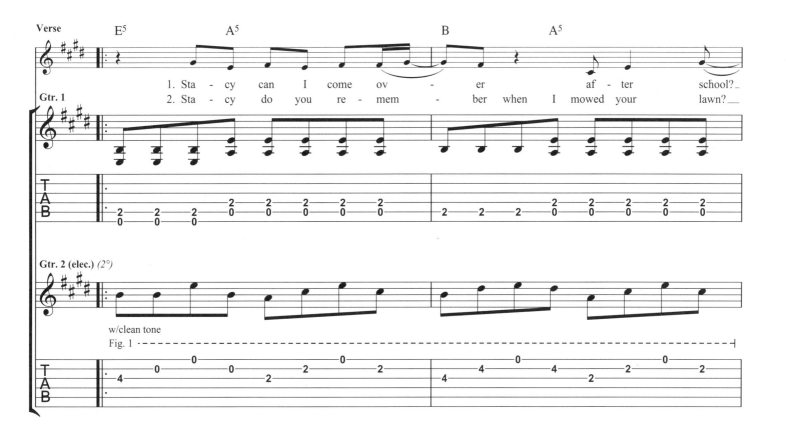

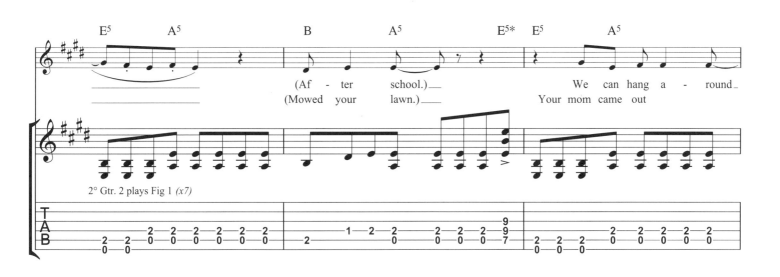

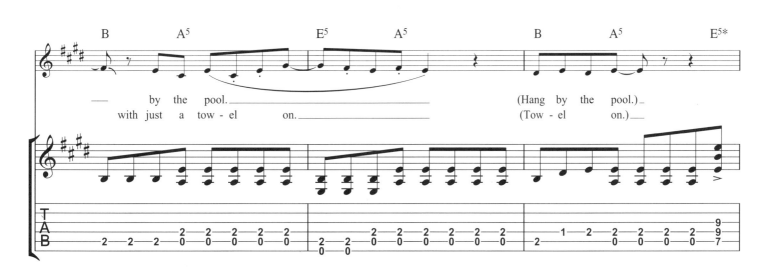

Did your mom get___ back   from her bus -'ness___ trip?___
I could tell she___ liked   me from the way she___ stared.___

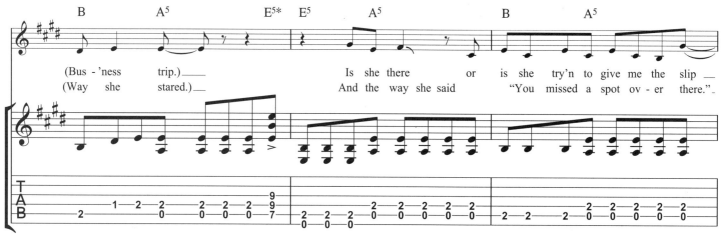

(Bus -'ness   trip.)___   Is she there   or   is she try'n to give me the slip ___
(Way she   stared.)___   And the way she said   "You missed a spot ov - er   there."_

Pre-chorus

(Give me the slip.)___ You know I'm   not the lit - tle boy___ that I
(Spot ov - er there.)___ And I   know   that you think it's just a

open out

used to be,   I'm   all___ grown___ up___ now,   ba - by can't you see.}
fan - ta - sy,   but since your dad walked out___ your mom could use a guy like me.}

TAKE ME OUT
WORDS & MUSIC BY ALEXANDER KAPRANOS & NICHOLAS McCARTHY

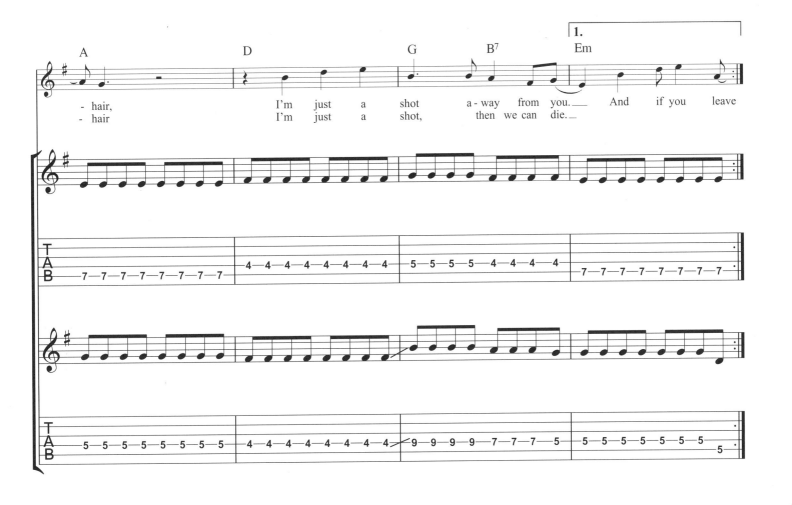

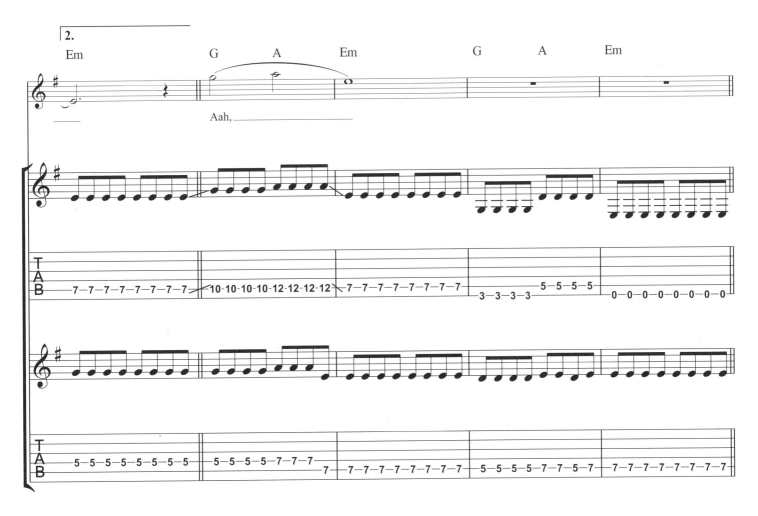

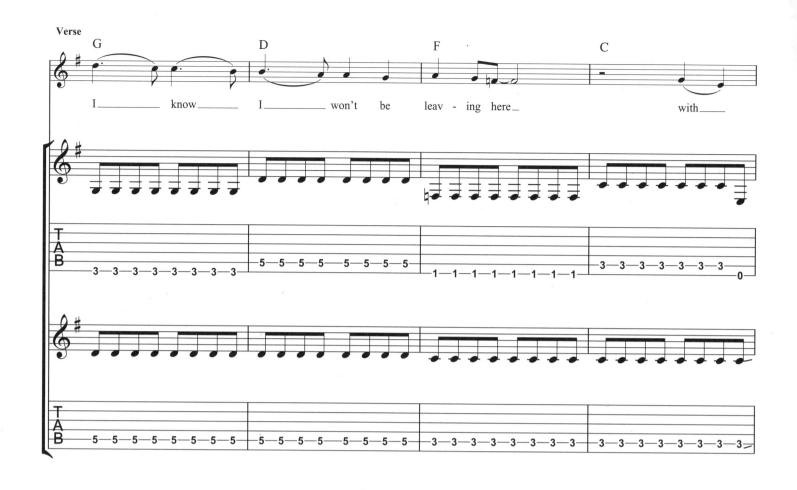

Verse

I_____ know_____ I_____ won't be leav - ing here___ with_____

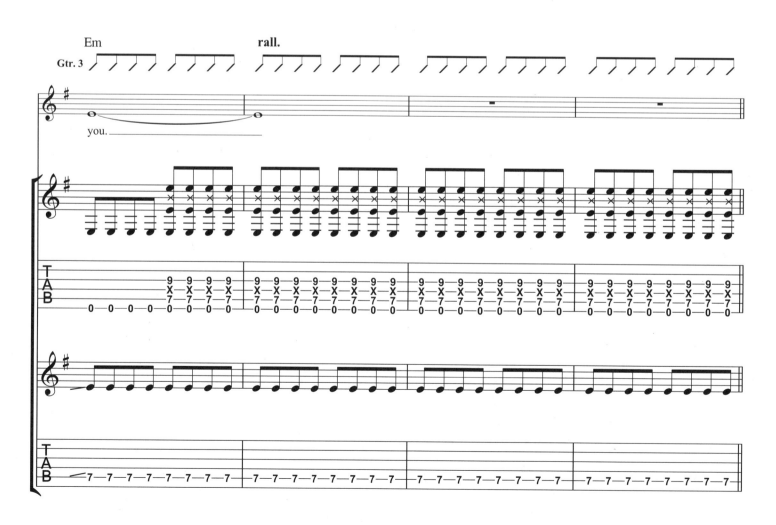

you._____

1. I say___ don't you know?___
2. I say___ you don't know,___
3. I say___ don't you know?___

You say___ you don't know.___ I say   take me out___
you say___ you don't know.___ I say   take me out___
You say___ you don't know.___ I say   take me out___

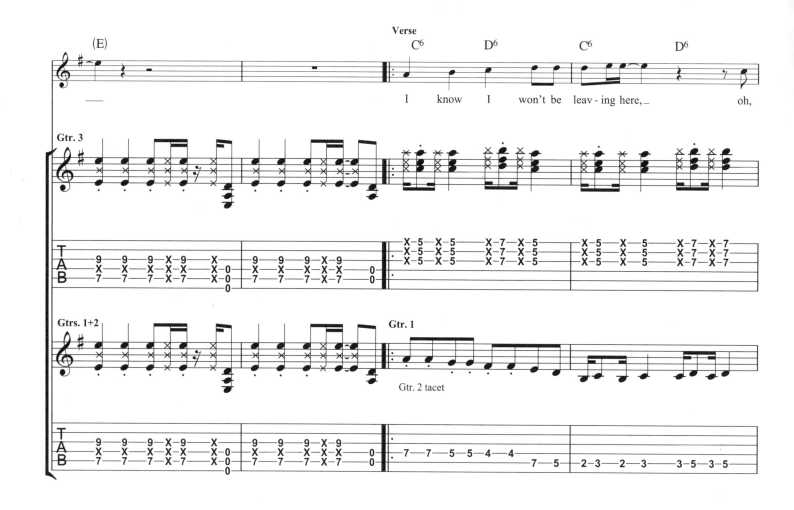

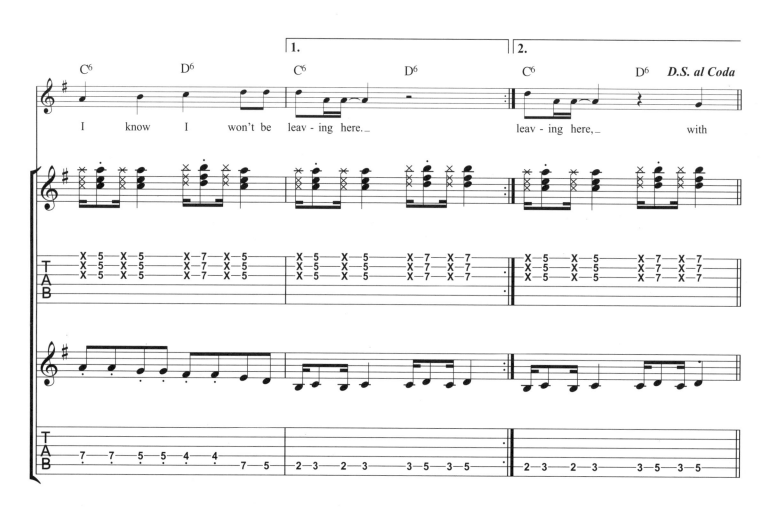

TIME IS RUNNING OUT

WORDS & MUSIC BY MATTHEW BELLAMY, CHRIS WOLSTENHOLME & DOMINIC HOWARD

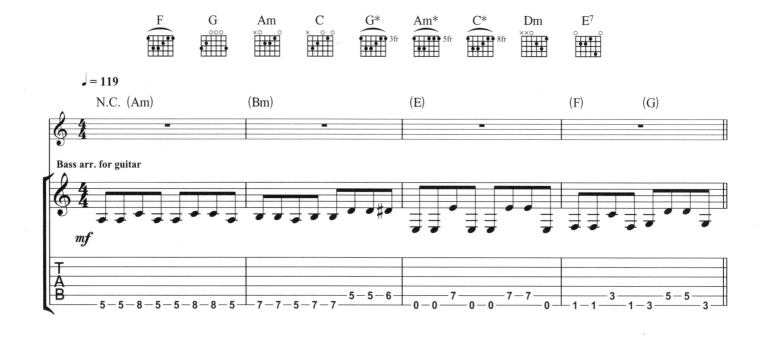

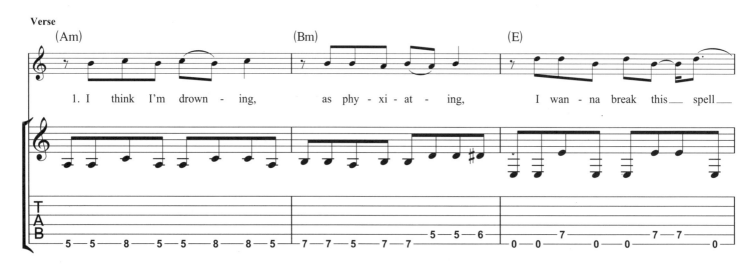

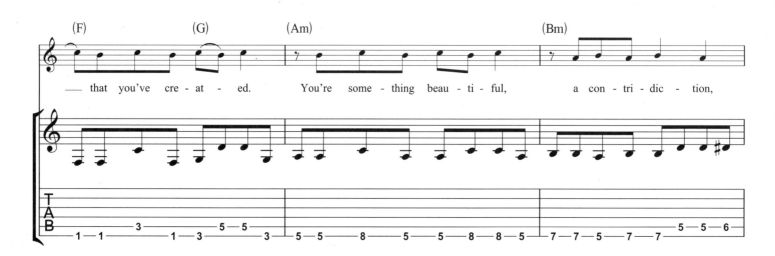

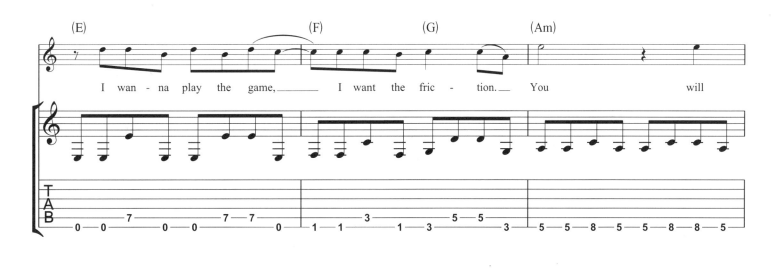

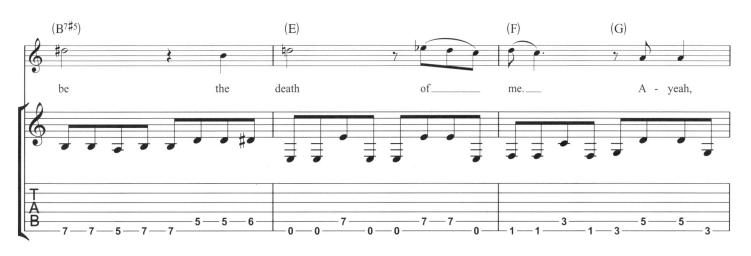

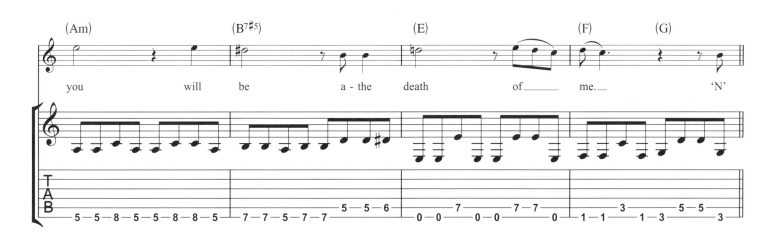

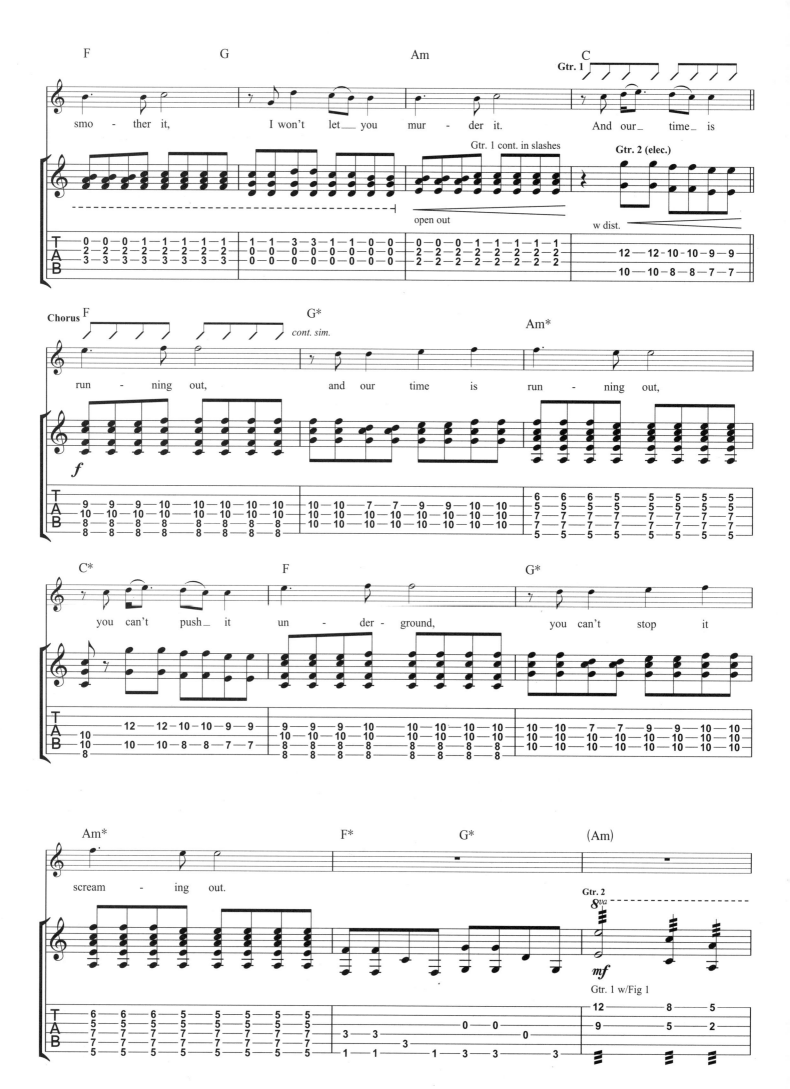

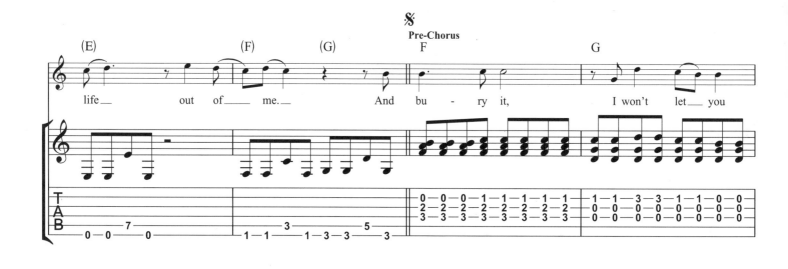

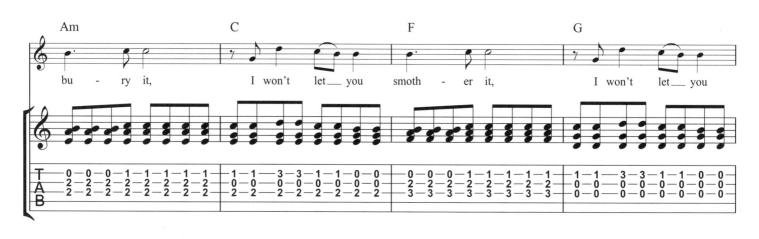

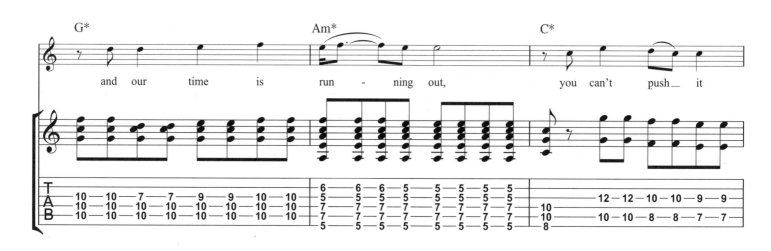

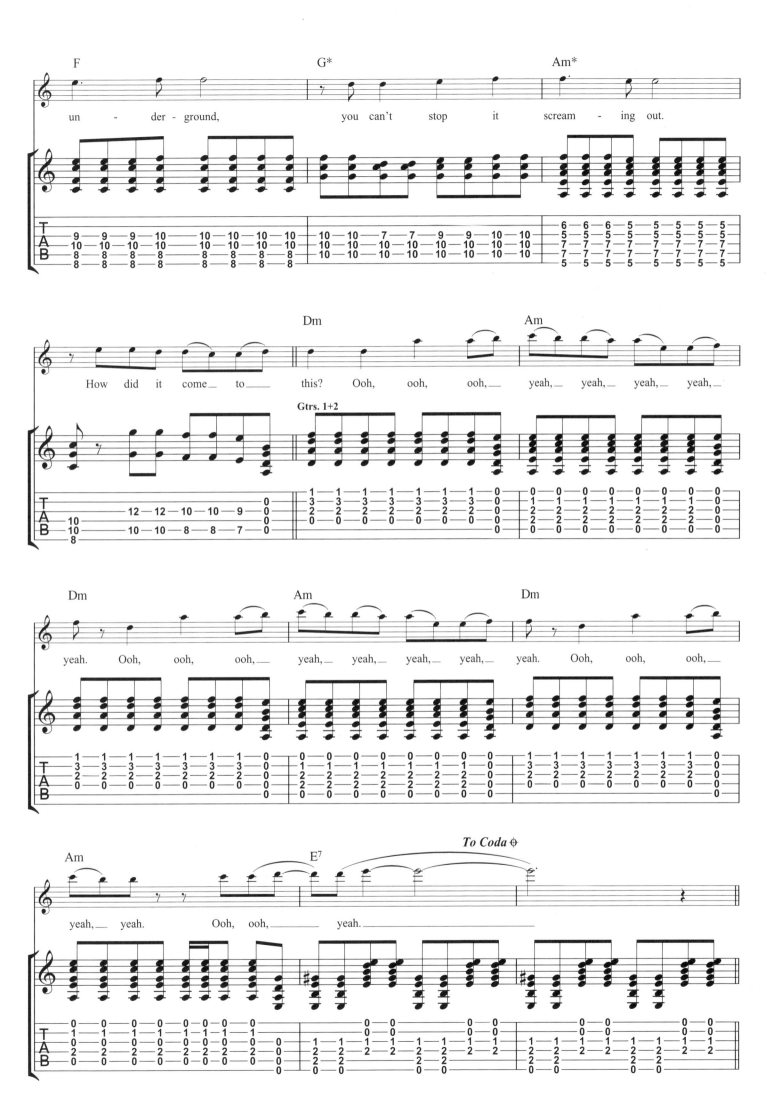

WARNING SIGN

WORDS & MUSIC BY GUY BERRYMAN, JON BUCKLAND, WILL CHAMPION & CHRIS MARTIN

* composite part

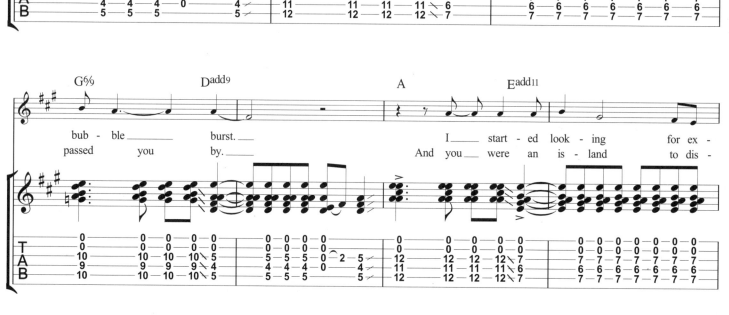

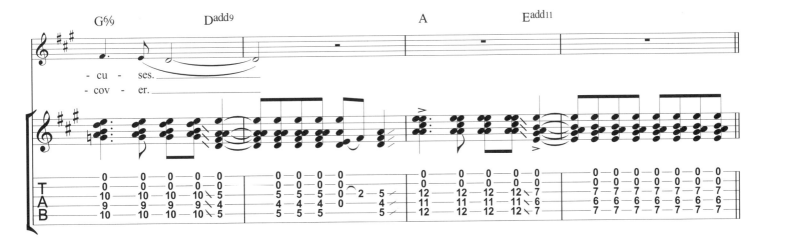

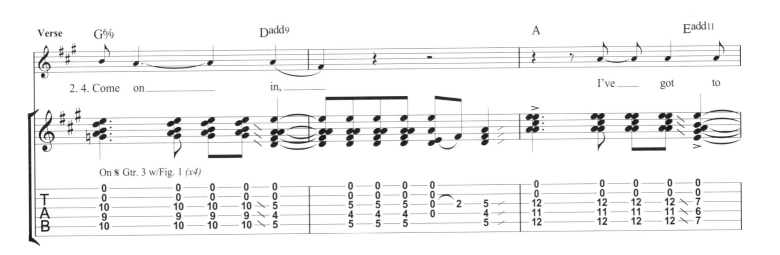

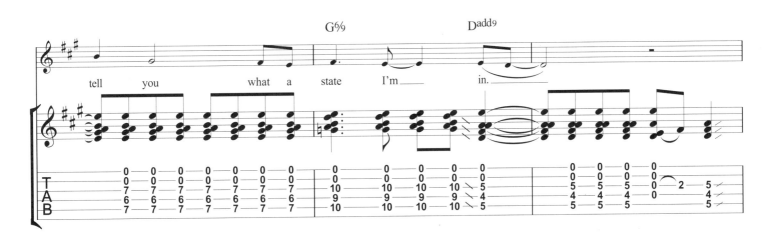

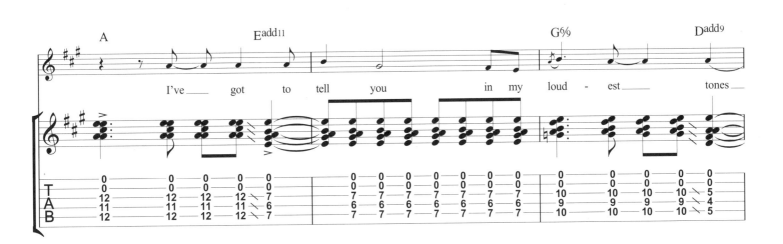

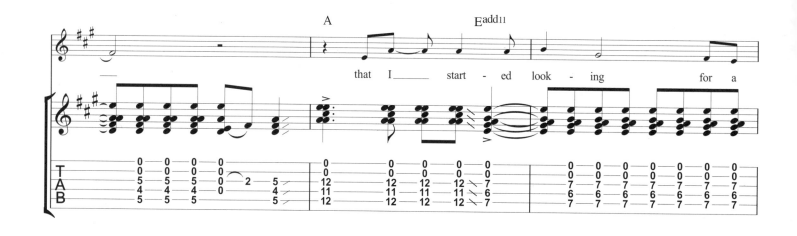

that I____ start - ed look - ing   for a

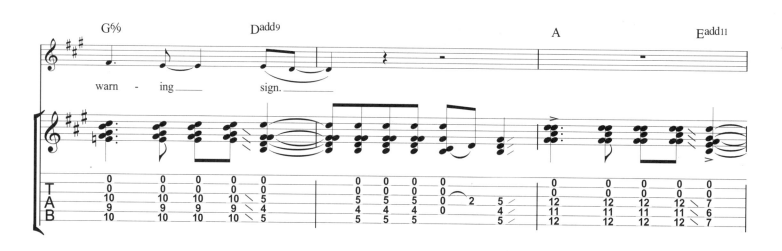

warn - ing____ sign.____

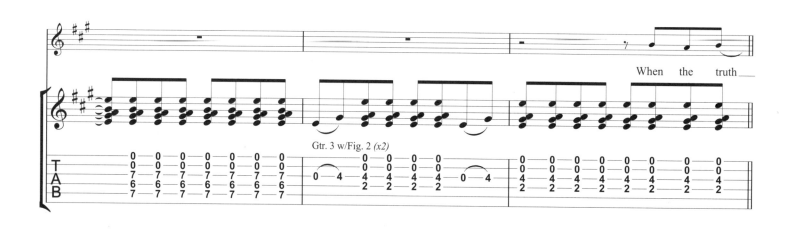

When the truth____

Gtr. 3 w/Fig. 2 *(x2)*

Chorus

____ is____

cont. sim.

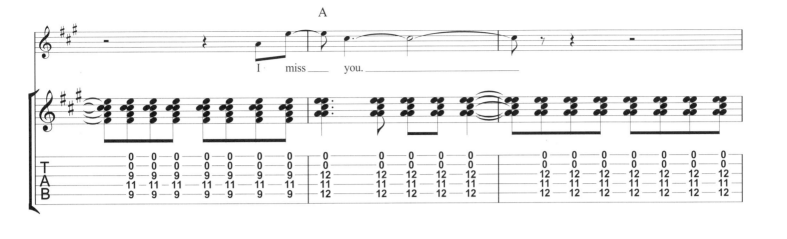

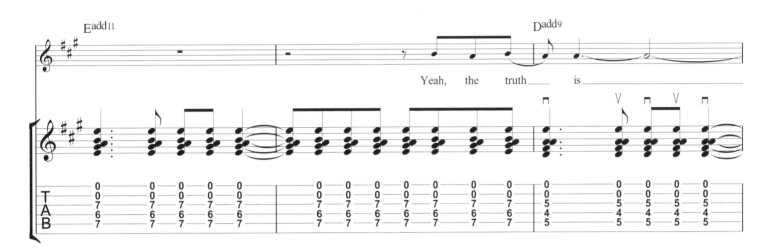

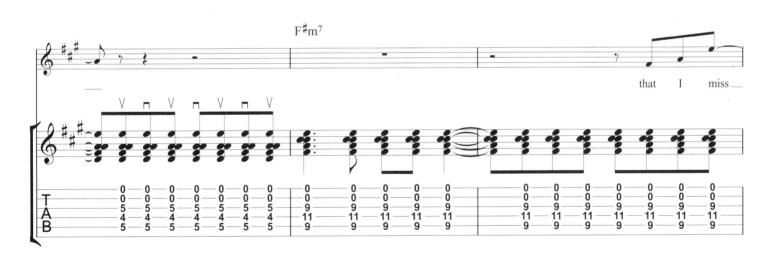

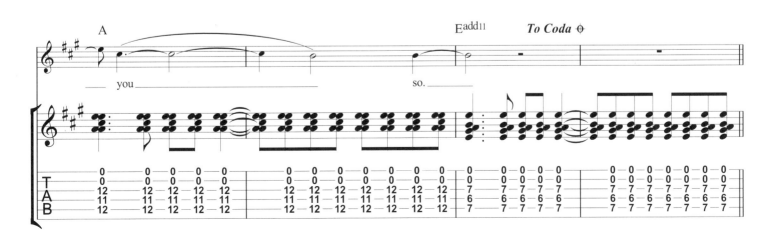

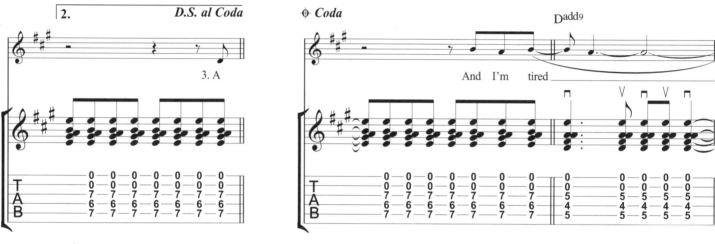

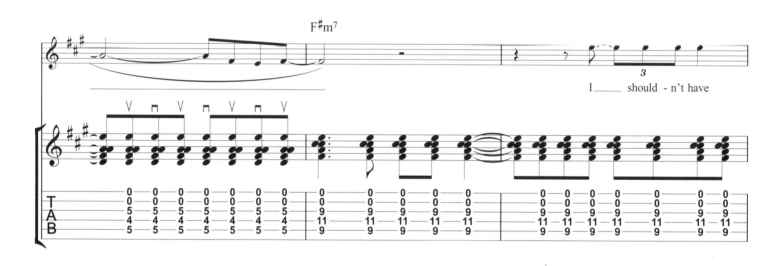

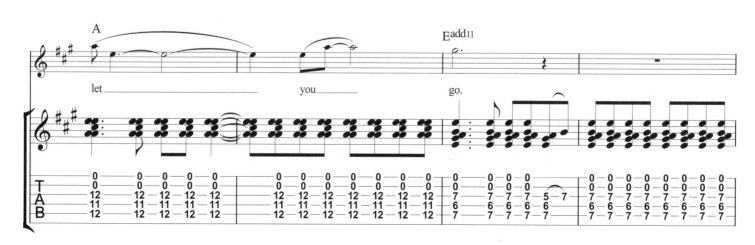

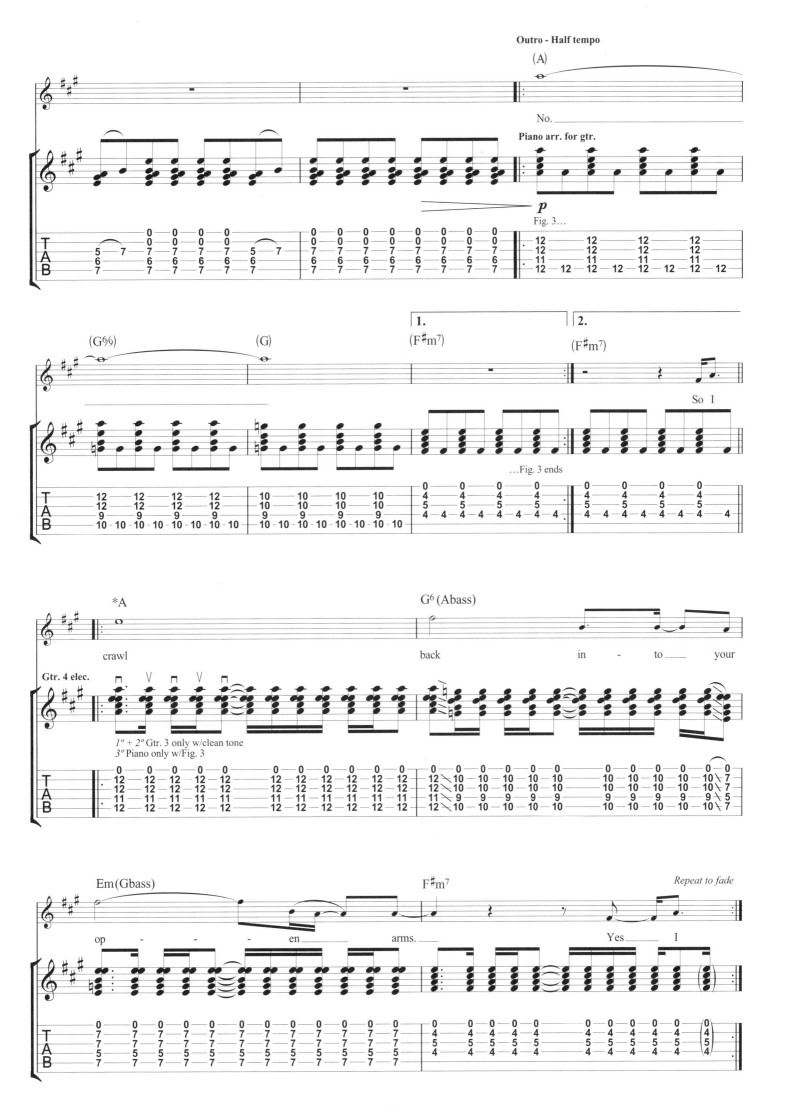

WASH IN THE RAIN

WORDS & MUSIC BY PAUL BUTLER & AARON FLETCHER

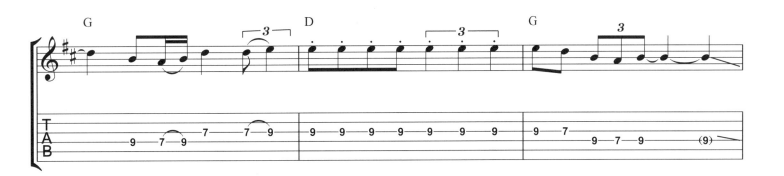

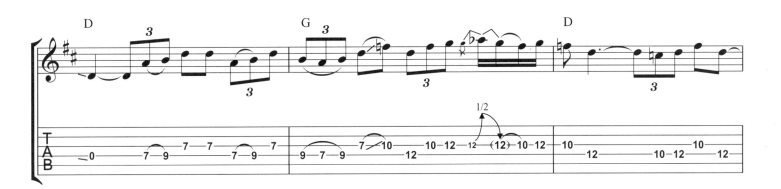

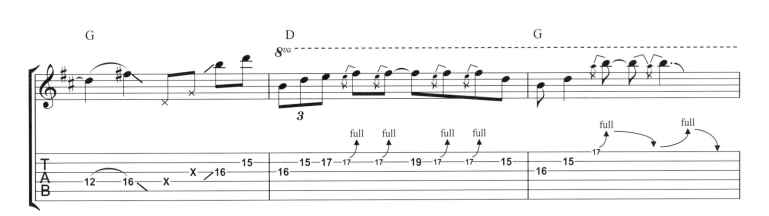

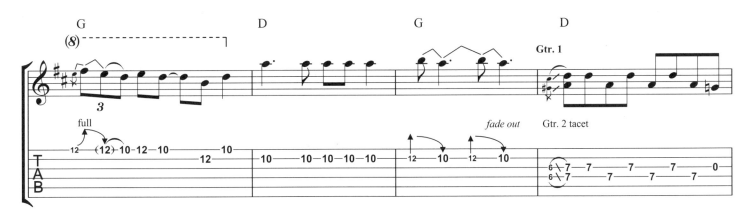

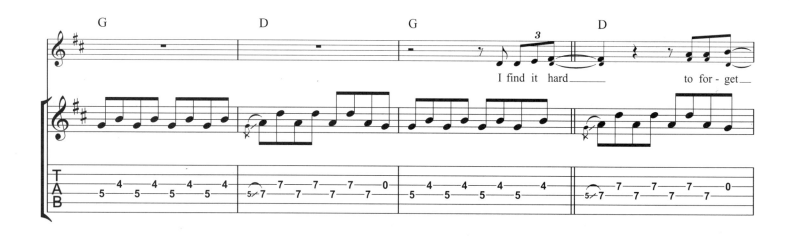

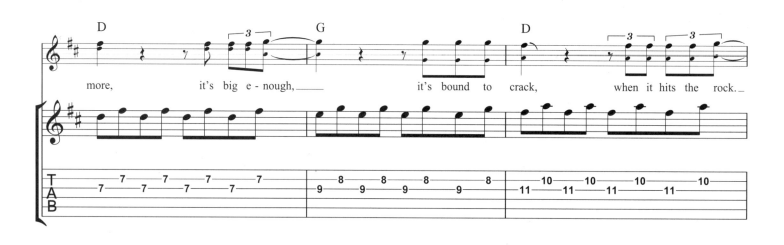

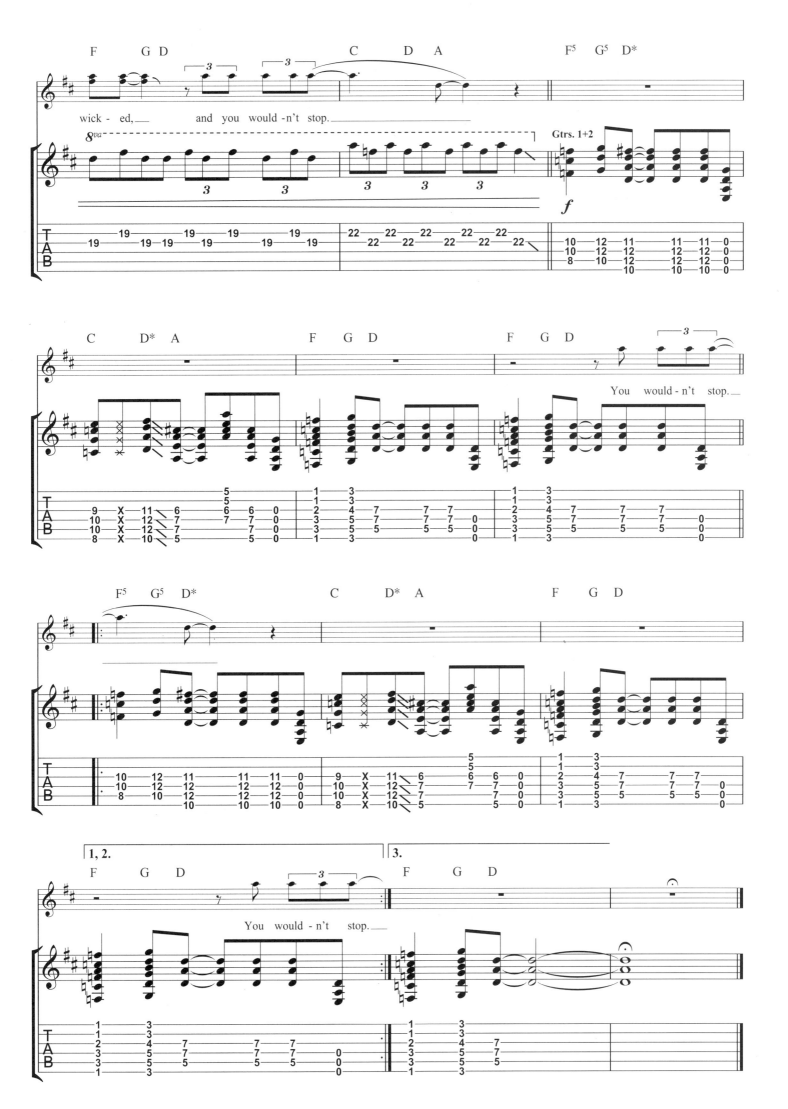

WONDERWALL
WORDS & MUSIC BY NOEL GALLAGHER

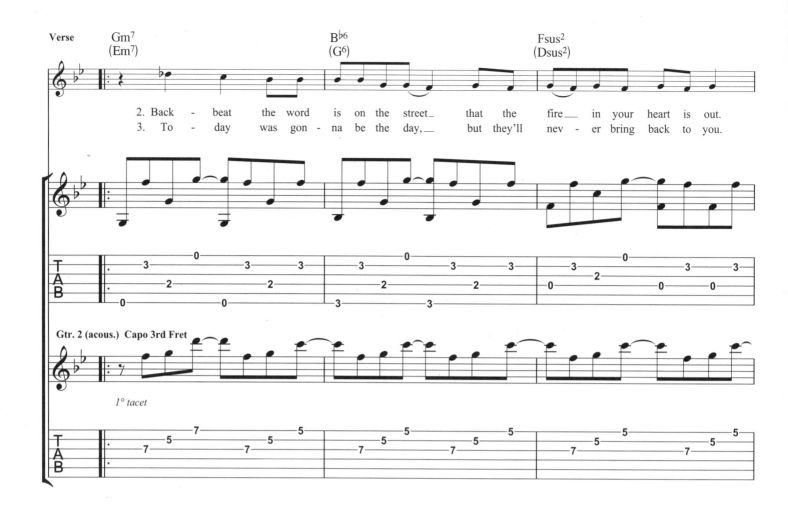

Verse

Gm⁷ (Em⁷) B♭⁶ (G⁶) Fsus² (Dsus²)

2. Back - beat the word is on the street__ that the fire__ in your heart is out.
3. To - day was gon - na be the day,__ but they'll nev - er bring back to you.

Gtr. 2 (acous.) Capo 3rd Fret

1° tacet

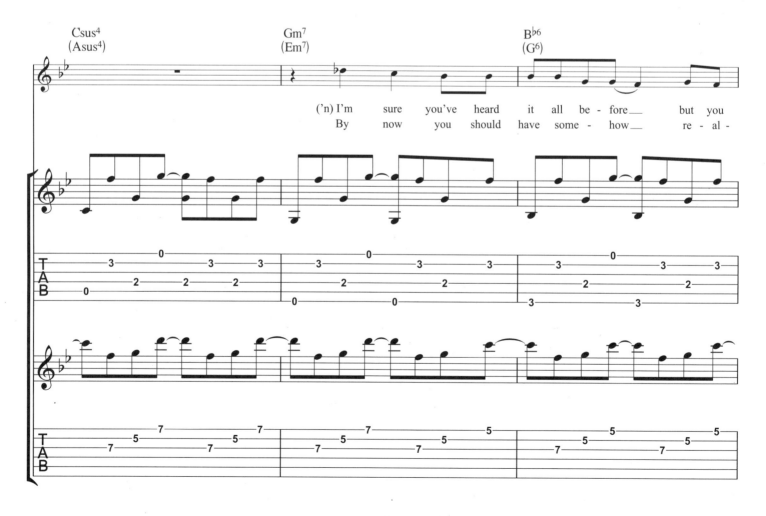

Csus⁴ (Asus⁴) Gm⁷ (Em⁷) B♭⁶ (G⁶)

('n) I'm sure you've heard it all be - fore__ but you
By now you should have some - how__ re - al -

nev - er real - ly had a doubt.
- ised what you got - ta do.

I don't be - lieve that a -

-ny - bo - dy feels the way I do a - bout you now.

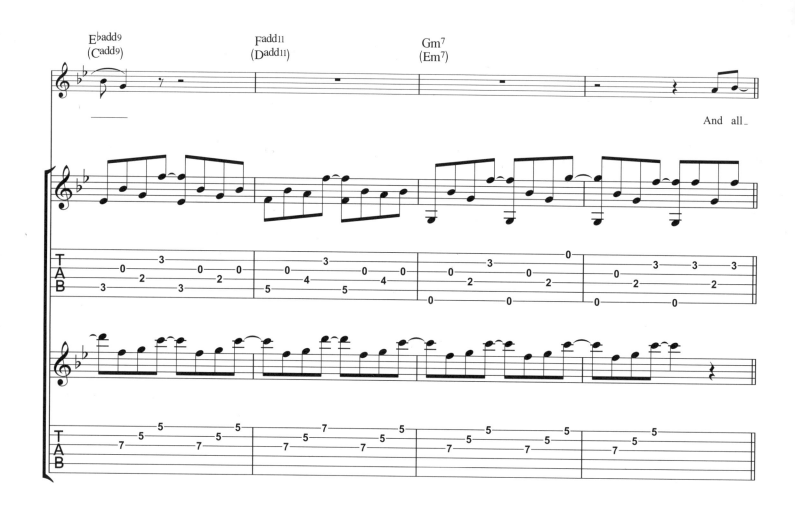

And all

Bridge

— the roads we have to walk are wind - ing,

and all_____ the lights__ that lead_____ the way are blind -

- ing.   And there are ma - ny things_____ that I____ would

like   to say to you____   but I don't know   how.____

Chorus

I said   may - be____

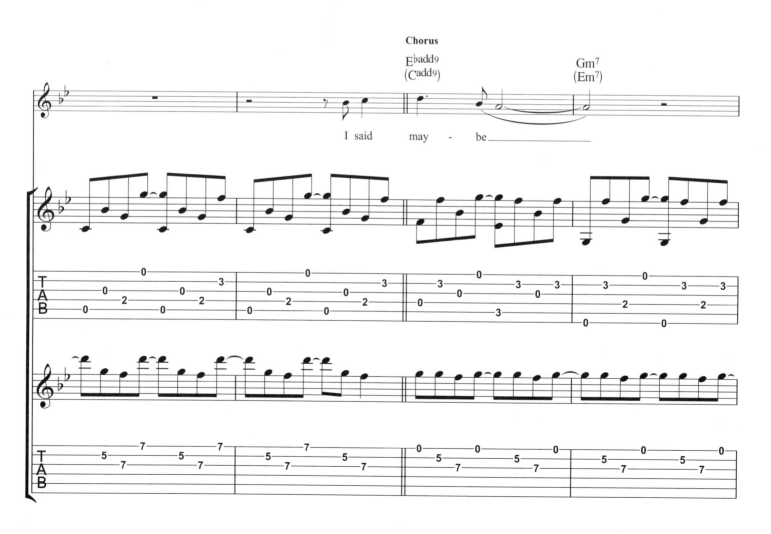

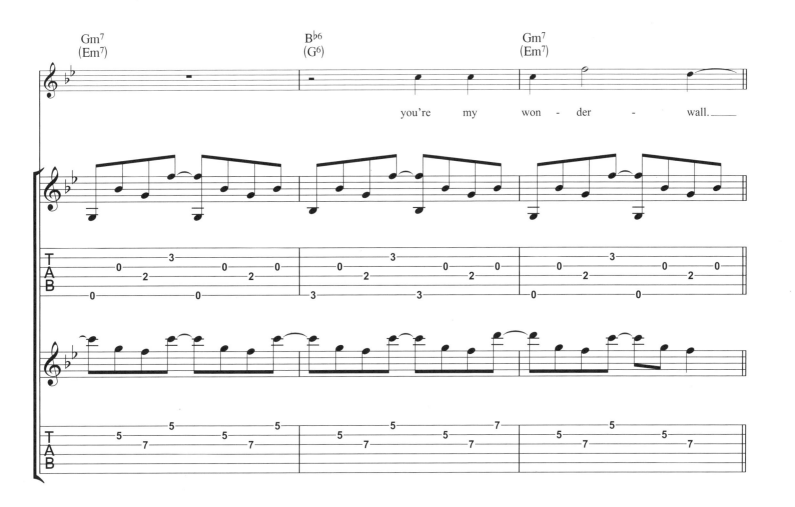

you're my won - der - wall. _____

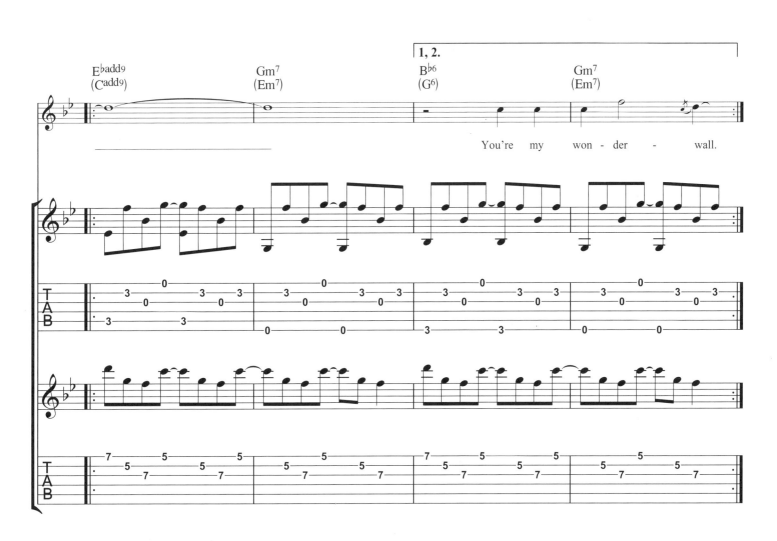

_____ You're my won - der - wall.

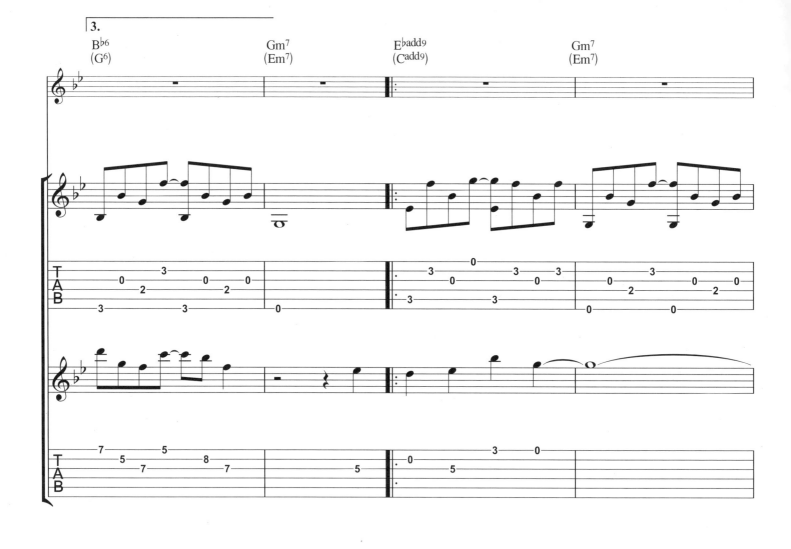

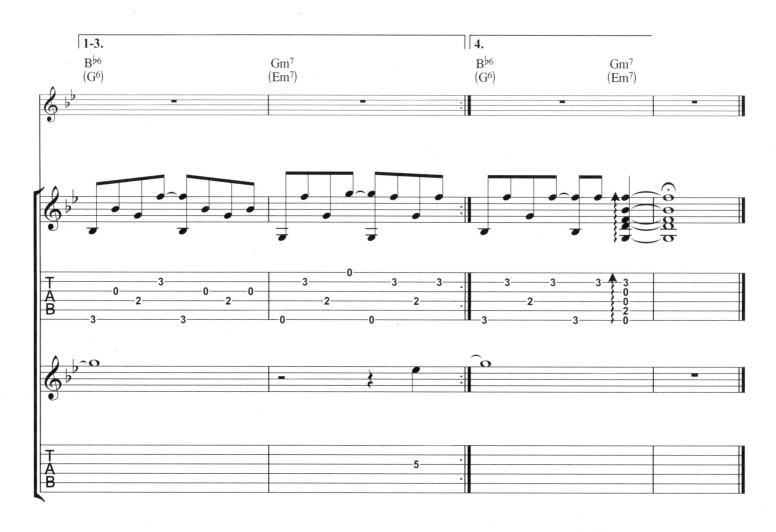